OLDBOURNE MATHEMATICAL SERIES

General Editor: G. T. Kneebone, *Bedford College, London*

THE ELEMENTARY THEORY OF NUMBERS,
POLYNOMIALS, AND RATIONAL FUNCTIONS

THE ELEMENTARY THEORY
OF
NUMBERS, POLYNOMIALS,
AND
RATIONAL FUNCTIONS

W. P. EAMES

Lakehead University, Ontario, Canada

AMERICAN ELSEVIER · NEW YORK

LIBRARY OF CONGRESS CATALOG CARD NUMBER: 68-19220

PRINTED IN GREAT BRITAIN

PREFACE

This book is written particularly for students pursuing undergraduate courses in algebra and the foundations of analysis. Much of the material has been given in lectures intended to cover that portion of the syllabus for the Special Degree in Mathematics of the University of London which is concerned with the integers, polynomials, and elementary algebraic structures, and I have supplemented this with material on the construction of the various number systems.

In the first chapter the set of integers is constructed using the Dedekind-Peano axioms, and we also consider some elementary properties of congruences. The real and complex number systems are developed in the second chapter. The techniques and results of the first two chapters serve to motivate much of the third chapter, which is on groups, rings, and fields. This chapter concludes with the characterization of the real number system as an ordered field. The last chapter is on polynomials, which are defined as sequences of ring elements. I have found that this treatment is the most acceptable to undergraduates, and helps emphasize the difference between polynomials and polynomial functions.

I wish to acknowledge here my indebtedness for the help given me by my students and colleagues at Sir John Cass College, in particular Mr C. Martin and Mr L. May, and by the editor, Dr G. T. Kneebone, and the publishers. I must also thank the University of London for permission to use problems set during the last few years.

CONTENTS

Preface   v

Chapter 1   The Integers

 1   Sets, relations, and functions   1
 2   The positive integers   5
 3   Addition and multiplication of the positive integers   7
 4   The integers   10
 5   The well-ordering of the positive integers   15
 6   The number of elements in a set   16
 7   The general associative and commutative laws   18
 8   Divisibility   24
 9   Prime and relatively prime integers   27
10   Least common multiples   29
11   Congruences and residue classes   30
12   The solution of congruences in one unknown   33

Chapter 2   The Rational, Real, and Complex Numbers

 1   The rational numbers   37
 2   The real numbers   40
 3   Sequences of real numbers   49
 4   Three inequalities between real numbers   52
 5   The complex numbers   54
 6   The geometry of the complex numbers   58
 7   The roots of unity   60

Chapter 3   Some Algebraic Structures

 1   Binary operations and groups   64
 2   Subgroups   70
 3   Groups of bijections   73
 4   Isomorphisms and homomorphisms   81
 5   Factor groups   86
 6   Rings and fields   93
 7   Ordered groups and rings   100

Chapter 4 Polynomials and Rational Functions

1 Polynomials 108
2 Polynomial functions 118
3 Polynomials over the field of complex numbers 123
4 Rational functions and partial fractions 124
5 Polynomials in several variables 128
6 Symmetric polynomials 131

Index of Symbols 139

General Index 141

CHAPTER 1

THE INTEGERS

1 Sets, relations, and functions

Any definition must ultimately depend on undefined entities. We will use the undefined terms *set* and *element* as in 'the set of all integers', 'the elements of a given set', etc., and assume that, given an element a and a set A, either a is an element of A, written $a \in A$, or it is not, written $a \notin A$. Usually sets will be denoted by capital letters $A, B, C, \ldots$, and elements by lower case letters $a, b, c, \ldots$. This may lead to some confusion if the elements of a set are themselves sets, but the context should resolve any ambiguity.

If the elements of a set can be listed $a, b, c, \ldots$, then the set will be denoted by $\{a, b, c, \ldots\}$. For example, $\{1, -1\}$ is the set whose elements are 1 and -1. The set of those elements which satisfy a given condition will be denoted by $\{x \mid x \text{ satisfies the condition}\}$. Thus the set $\{x \mid x \text{ is a real number such that } x^2 = 1\}$ is just the set $\{1, -1\}$.

If the elements a, b are the same element then we write $a = b$, otherwise $a \neq b$. If A, B are sets and every element of A is also an element of B, then A is said to be a *subset* of B and we write $A \subseteq B$ or $B \supseteq A$. If A, B contain the same elements, then they are said to be *equal*, and this is written $A = B$. Thus $A = B$ if and only if $A \subseteq B$ and $B \subseteq A$.

The set of those elements which are in at least one of the sets A, B is denoted by $A \cup B$ and called the *union* of A and B. That is, $A \cup B = \{x \mid x \in A \text{ or } x \in B\}$. The word 'or' is used here in the common mathematical sense of 'and/or': if $x \in A$ and $x \in B$, then $x \in A \cup B$.

The set of elements common to A and B is denoted by $A \cap B$ and called the *intersection* of A and B. That is, $A \cap B = \{x \mid x \in A \text{ and } x \in B\}$.

If C is a set whose elements are themselves sets, then by the *union* of the sets in C we mean the set of those elements which are in at least one of the sets in C, and by the *intersection* of the sets in C we mean the set of those elements common to all the sets in C. Two sets are said to be *disjoint* if they have no common elements, and a set C of sets is said to be *pairwise-disjoint*, or the sets in C are said to be pairwise-disjoint, if, whenever $A \in C$ and $B \in C$, then either $A = B$ or A and B are disjoint.

An *ordered pair* of elements from a set A is a set of the form $\{\{a, b\}, \{a\}\}$, where $a, b \in A$. Such an ordered pair is denoted by $\langle a, b \rangle$. We note that it depends not only on the elements a, b, but also on the order in which they are displayed. That is, $\langle a, b \rangle = \langle c, d \rangle$ if and only if $a = c$ and $b = d$. For example, the set of all ordered pairs from the set $\{a, b\}$ is

$$\{\langle a, a \rangle, \langle a, b \rangle, \langle b, a \rangle, \langle b, b \rangle\}.$$

A *relation* on a set A is a set of ordered pairs of elements from A. Thus $\{\langle a, a \rangle, \langle b, a \rangle\}$ is a relation on $\{a, b\}$. Sometimes a relation is denoted by a symbol such as α or $\equiv$, and we then write $a \alpha b$ or $a \equiv b$ if and only if $\langle a, b \rangle$ is in the relation. If we wrote the above relation as α, then we would have $a \alpha a$ and $b \alpha a$; but, if $a \neq b$, we would not have $a \alpha b$ or $b \alpha b$. A relation is sometimes referred to as if it were a symbol in phrases like 'the relation α', and the connection between the relation and the symbol is always understood to be as above.

An *equivalence relation* on a set A is a relation R on A with the properties:

(i) $\langle a, a \rangle \in R$ for all $a \in A$;
(ii) if $\langle a, b \rangle \in R$, then $\langle b, a \rangle \in R$;
(iii) if $\langle a, b \rangle \in R$ and $\langle b, c \rangle \in R$, then $\langle a, c \rangle \in R$.

Thus a relation α is an equivalence relation on A if and only if

(i) $a \alpha a$ for all $a \in A$;
(ii) if $a \alpha b$, then $b \alpha a$;
(iii) if $a \alpha b$ and $b \alpha c$, then $a \alpha c$.

EXAMPLES. (i) If $a \neq b$, then the relation $\{\langle a, a \rangle, \langle b, a \rangle\}$ on the set $\{a, b\}$ is not an equivalence relation – neither $\langle b, b \rangle$ nor $\langle a, b \rangle$ is in it. The relations $\{\langle a, a \rangle, \langle b, b \rangle\}$ and $\{\langle a, a \rangle, \langle b, b \rangle, \langle a, b \rangle, \langle b, a \rangle\}$ are equivalence relations on $\{a, b\}$, and it is easy to see that they are the only equivalence relations on $\{a, b\}$.

(ii) Let **Z** be the set of all integers. (The properties of the integers and real numbers which are used in some of the examples and exercises of this section are probably known to the reader. They will be proved later.) Define a relation α on **Z** by the condition '$a \alpha b$ if and only if $a - b$ is even'. This relation is easily seen to be an equivalence relation:
(a) $a \alpha a$ for all integers a, since 0 is an even integer;
(b) if $a - b$ is even, then so is $b - a$;
(c) the sum of two even integers is even, so, if $a - b$ and $b - c$ are even, then $(a - b) + (b - c) = a - c$ is also even.

Let R be an equivalence relation on a set A, let $a \in A$, and let $[a]$ be the set $\{x \mid x \in A \text{ and } \langle a, x \rangle \in R\}$. Clearly, $[a]$ is a subset of A which depends on R and a. A subset of A which is of the form $[a]$ for some appropriate a is called an *equivalence class*. Suppose that two equivalence classes $[a]$ and

[b], defined by the same relation R, have an element c in common. Then $\langle a, c \rangle \in R$ and $\langle b, c \rangle \in R$. By properties (ii) and (iii) of R we have $\langle b, a \rangle \in R$. Let $d \in [a]$. Then $\langle a, d \rangle \in R$, so that $\langle b, d \rangle \in R$ and thus $d \in [b]$. Since d can be any element of $[a]$, we have shown that $[a] \subseteq [b]$. Similarly, $[b] \subseteq [a]$, so that $[a] = [b]$. Thus the set of equivalence classes defined by R is pairwise-disjoint. Also, every element in A is in an equivalence class since, by (i), $a \in [a]$, and so the union of all the equivalence classes defined by R is just A. To summarize: *an equivalence relation R on a set A partitions that set into pairwise-disjoint subsets, two elements a, b being in the same subset if and only if $\langle a, b \rangle \in R$.*

On the other hand, let C be a set of pairwise-disjoint subsets of a set A whose union is A, and let R be the relation $\{\langle a, b \rangle \mid a, b$ are in the same set in $C\}$. R is easily seen to be an equivalence relation on A and, furthermore, the equivalence classes defined by R are the sets in C. Thus the equivalence classes defined by an equivalence relation fully describe that relation, that is, the relation can be obtained from its equivalence classes.

EXAMPLE. Consider the equivalence relation defined on the set $\mathbf{Z}$ of integers above. The equivalence class [0] consists of all those integers n such that $0 - n$ is even. Thus [0] is the set of all even integers. The class [1] consists of all those integers n such that $1 - n$ is even, so [1] is the set of all odd integers. Since every integer is either even or odd, there are only two equivalence classes, [0] and [1].

We now consider another special type of relation. By a *function from a set A to a set B* we mean a relation f on $A \cup B$ with the property that, given $a \in A$, there is one and only one element $b \in B$ such that $\langle a, b \rangle \in f$.[1]

Thus a function associates with each element of A a unique element of B. This suggests the notation that is commonly used: if f is a function from A to B and $a \in A$, then the unique element b such that $\langle a, b \rangle \in f$ is denoted by $f(a)$. A function f from A to B is said to be:

(i) a *surjection* if, for each $b \in B$, there is at least one element $a \in A$ such that $f(a) = b$;
(ii) an *injection* if, whenever $f(a) = f(b)$, then $a = b$;
(iii) a *bijection* if it is both an injection and a surjection.

A surjection from A to B is sometimes said to be a function from A *onto B*, and a bijection from A to B is sometimes termed a *one-one* function from A to B.

---

[1] In some books the concept of function is defined in terms of a relation from a set to a set; see, for example, Rotman and Kneebone, *The Theory of Sets and Transfinite Numbers* (London, 1966), p. 27.

EXAMPLES. Consider the following functions from the set of all real numbers to that set:

(i) The set of all ordered pairs of the form $\langle x, x^2 \rangle$, x ranging over all real numbers. Here $f(x) = x^2$ for all real numbers x. The function f is not an injection because, for example, $f(1) = f(-1)$. It is not a surjection because there is no real number x such that $f(x) = -1$.

(ii) The function defined by the condition $f(x) = x^3$, that is to say, the function that is the set of all ordered pairs of the form $\langle x, x^3 \rangle$. This function is a bijection.

(iii) The function defined by $f(x) = x^3 - x^2$ is a surjection but not an injection, and the function $f(x) = e^x$ is an injection but not a surjection.

EXERCISES

1. Which of the relations α defined below on the set of all integers are equivalence relations?

(i) $a \, \alpha \, b$ if and only if $a + b$ is even;
(ii) $a \, \alpha \, b$ if and only if $a \geqslant b$;
(iii) $a \, \alpha \, b$ if and only if $a - b$ is odd or 0;
(iv) $a \, \alpha \, b$ never occurs, that is, the relation is empty.

By considering the above relations, show that, given any two of the three properties of an equivalence relation, there is a relation having these two properties but not the remaining property. Thus prove that no one of the three properties in the definition of equivalence relation can be deduced from the other two.

2. Show that, if a relation R on a set A has the properties:

(i) if $a \in A$, then $\langle a, b \rangle \in R$ for some $b \in A$;
(ii) if $\langle a, b \rangle \in R$, then $\langle b, a \rangle \in R$;
(iii) if $\langle a, b \rangle \in R$ and $\langle b, c \rangle \in R$, then $\langle a, c \rangle \in R$;
then R is an equivalence relation on A.

3. Find the set of all ordered pairs of elements from $\{a, b, c, d\}$, and the set of all possible equivalence relations on $\{a, b, c, d\}$.

4. Let f be a function from a set A to a set B, and let α be the relation defined on A by '$a \, \alpha \, b$ if and only if $f(a) = f(b)$'. Show that α is an equivalence relation on A, and that the function g from the set of equivalence classes to B defined by

$$g([a]) = f(a)$$

is an injection.

5. Let f be a function from a set A to a set B, and let C be a subset of A and E a subset of B. Let

$$f(C) = \{x \,|\, \text{there is an element } c \in C \text{ such that } f(c) = x\}$$

and
$$f^{-1}(E) = \{x \,|\, f(x) \in E\}.$$

Show that, for all subsets C, D of A and all subsets E, F of B:

(i) $f(C \cup D) = f(C) \cup f(D)$;
(ii) $f(C \cap D) \subseteq f(C) \cap f(D)$;

(iii) $f^{-1}(E \cup F) = f^{-1}(E) \cup f^{-1}(F)$;
(iv) $f^{-1}(E \cap F) = f^{-1}(E) \cap f^{-1}(F)$;
(v) $f(f^{-1}(E)) \subseteq E$;
(vi) $f^{-1}(f(C)) \supseteq C$.

Show, by considering appropriate examples, that equality cannot be asserted in general in (ii), (v), and (vi) above.

6. Let B be the set of all subsets of a set A, and let f be a function from B to B with the property that, if $C \subseteq D \subseteq A$, then $f(C) \subseteq f(D)$. Let E be the intersection of all those sets C with the property that $f(C) \subseteq C$. Show that there are such sets C, so that E exists, and show that $f(E) = E$.

2   The positive integers

The reader is undoubtedly familiar with the elementary properties of the integers – so familiar, in fact, that in attempting to prove any theorem about them he may find it difficult to know precisely what can be assumed and what there is to prove. Thus we must define the integers by properties which are accepted as postulates and prove all the relevant theorems from these.

First we will define the positive integers. Our definition, due to Dedekind and Peano, is suggested by the way the positive integers are used in counting: the physical act of counting proceeds by first counting '1', then its successor '2', then the successor of 2, and so on, each positive integer, except 1, having one and only one immediate predecessor in the list

$$1, 2, 3, 4, \ldots,$$

but 1 having no predecessor. Also, each positive integer occurs eventually in this list; that is, if a set of positive integers contains 1 and, with n, the successor of n, then this set contains every positive integer.

DEFINITION. The *set of positive integers* is a set $\mathbf{Z}^+$ and a function s from $\mathbf{Z}^+$ to $\mathbf{Z}^+$ with the properties:

P1: There is an element $1 \in \mathbf{Z}^+$ such that, for all $n \in \mathbf{Z}^+$, $1 \neq s(n)$;

P2: If $n, m \in \mathbf{Z}^+$ and $s(n) = s(m)$, then $n = m$;

P3: If $Q \subseteq \mathbf{Z}^+$ and $1 \in Q$ and, whenever $n \in Q$, then $s(n) \in Q$, then $Q = \mathbf{Z}^+$.

The distinguished element 1 is called the *initial* element of the set of positive integers, s is called the *successor* function, and $s(n)$ is called the *successor of n*. P1 states that the initial element is not the successor of any element in $\mathbf{Z}^+$, P2 states that s is an injection from $\mathbf{Z}^+$ to $\mathbf{Z}^+$, and P3 is a formal expression of the statement that every element of $\mathbf{Z}^+$ must occur in any list which contains 1 and, with n, the successor of n.

There are three points to note about this definition:

(i) The definition does not assert that the set of positive integers exists.

Like all definitions, it merely gives conditions under which a term – in this case 'the set of positive integers' – can be applied to a particular mathematical entity. Any proof of the existence of the set of positive integers must necessarily rest on the assumption of the existence of some mathematical object. We prefer to assume directly that the set of positive integers does exist, and *we therefore postulate the existence of a set* $\mathbf{Z}^+$ *and a function s satisfying* P1, P2, *and* P3. Henceforth the term 'the set of positive integers' is meant to refer to this postulated set $\mathbf{Z}^+$ and this postulated function s. As usual, we denote the successor $s(1)$ of 1 by 2, $s(2)$ by 3, and so on, so that $\mathbf{Z}^+$ can be displayed as $\{1, 2, 3, \ldots\}$.

(ii) The definition refers to *the* set of positive integers as if it were unique. In (i) we chose one particular set of positive integers and it might therefore be expected that this is the only possible set. This is not the case. For example, the set $\{2, 3, 4, \ldots\}$, with the obvious successor function and initial element 2 (which must therefore be renamed 1), satisfies the three conditions. Thus the set of positive integers is not unique, but all our subsequent remarks should be taken to refer to that particular set of positive integers which was chosen in (i).

(iii) The definition of the term 'the set of positive integers' refers not just to the set $\mathbf{Z}^+$, but to $\mathbf{Z}^+$ and the function s. Now we are going to misuse this term and refer to the elements of $\mathbf{Z}^+$ as *positive integers* and to $\mathbf{Z}^+$ as the set of positive integers, the successor function being understood.

THEOREM 1. *Let n be a positive integer. Then:*
(i) *if $n \neq 1$ there is a unique positive integer m such that $n = s(m)$*;
(ii) $s(n) \neq n$.

Proof. To prove (i), let Q be the set containing 1 and all those elements of $\mathbf{Z}^+$ which are of the form $s(n)$ for $n \in \mathbf{Z}^+$. Then Q satisfies the conditions in P3: $1 \in Q$ from the definition of Q and, if $n \in Q$, then $s(n) \in Q$, since Q contains all successors. Thus $Q = \mathbf{Z}^+$, and we have shown that every positive integer, except 1, is the successor of a positive integer. That $s(m)$ uniquely determines m is just the statement P2.

To prove (ii), let Q be the set of those $n \in \mathbf{Z}^+$ such that $s(n) \neq n$. Again, Q satisfies the conditions in P3: $s(1) \neq 1$ since 1 is not the successor of any positive integer, and, if $s(n) \neq n$, then $s(s(n)) \neq s(n)$, because if $s(s(n)) = s(n)$ then, by P2, we would have $s(n) = n$. Thus $Q = \mathbf{Z}^+$, and the proof is complete. □

Note that the proofs of (i) and (ii) above are of the same type: it was required to show, in each case, that a certain statement $S(n)$ holds for all $n \in \mathbf{Z}^+$. This was accomplished by showing that P3 applies to the set of those n for which $S(n)$ holds. A proof of this type is called an *induction proof* or a *proof by induction on n*, and P3 is sometimes called the *induction postulate* or *the principle of induction*. Most of the theorems of this chapter are proved by induction, Theorems 11 and 25 being particularly interesting examples.

EXERCISES

1. Give an example of a set and a function which satisfy P1 and P2 but not P3, and thus show that P3 cannot be deduced from P1 and P2. Similarly show that P1 cannot be deduced from P2 and P3, and that P2 cannot be deduced from P1 and P3.

2. Show that $\mathbf{Z}^+$ contains only one initial element.

3   Addition and multiplication of the positive integers

THEOREM 2. *Let n be a positive integer. Then there is one and only one function f from $\mathbf{Z}^+$ to $\mathbf{Z}^+$ such that*:
A1: $f(1) = s(n)$;
A2: $f(s(m)) = s(f(m))$ *for all $m \in \mathbf{Z}^+$.*

Proof. First we show that there is at least one function f satisfying A1 and A2. We proceed by induction on n. If $n = 1$, then the successor function satisfies A1 and A2: $s(1) = s(1)$, and $s(s(m)) = s(s(m))$ for all $m \in \mathbf{Z}^+$. Now suppose that n is a positive integer which has associated with it a function f satisfying A1 and A2. Consider the function $f(s(m))$. By A1 and A2,

$$f(s(1)) = s(f(1)) = s(s(n)),$$

so that $f(s(m))$ satisfies A1 if n is replaced by $s(n)$. Also

$$f(s(s(m))) = s(f(s(m)))$$

for all $m \in \mathbf{Z}^+$, by A2, so that $f(s(m))$ satisfies A2. Thus, by the principle of induction, each positive integer n can be associated with at least one function f satisfying A1 and A2.

Now to show that f is uniquely determined by n. Suppose that f, g are functions from $\mathbf{Z}^+$ to $\mathbf{Z}^+$ such that:

$$f(1) = s(n);$$
$$f(s(m)) = s(f(m)) \text{ for all } m \in \mathbf{Z}^+;$$
$$g(1) = s(n);$$
and $\qquad g(s(m)) = s(g(m))$ for all $m \in \mathbf{Z}^+$.

We must show that $f(m) = g(m)$ for all $m \in \mathbf{Z}^+$. We proceed by induction on m. Clearly $f(1) = g(1)$. Suppose that $f(m) = g(m)$. Then

$$g(s(m)) = s(g(m)) = s(f(m)) = f(s(m)).$$

Thus $f(m) = g(m)$ for all $m \in \mathbf{Z}^+$, by the principle of induction. $\square$

DEFINITION. The *sum*[1] $n + m$ of the positive integers n, m is the positive integer $f(m)$, where f is the function considered in Theorem 2.

Theorem 2 states that the sum $n + m$ exists for all positive integers n, m and that it is uniquely determined by the ordered pair $\langle n, m \rangle$. Note the lack of symmetry in the definition of $n + m$ – it is not at all obvious that $n + m = m + n$.

THEOREM 3. *If n, m, r are positive integers, then*:
(i) $(n + m) + r = n + (m + r)$;
(ii) $n + m = m + n$;
(iii) *if $n + m = n + r$, then $m = r$*.

Proof. First we note that, in terms of the symbol $+$, the properties A1 and A2 can be written:
A1: $n + 1 = s(n)$;
A2: $n + (m + 1) = (n + m) + 1$ for all $m \in \mathbf{Z}^+$.

To prove (i), we fix n, m, and proceed by induction on r. First we must show that $(n + m) + 1 = n + (m + 1)$; this is just A2. Now suppose that $(n + m) + r = n + (m + r)$. Then

$$
\begin{aligned}
(n + m) + s(r) &= (n + m) + (r + 1) &&\text{by A1} \\
&= ((n + m) + r) + 1 &&\text{by A2} \\
&= (n + (m + r)) + 1 \\
&= n + ((m + r) + 1) &&\text{by A2} \\
&= n + (m + (r + 1)) &&\text{by A2} \\
&= n + (m + s(r)) &&\text{by A1.}
\end{aligned}
$$

This, by the principle of induction, proves (i).

We prove (ii) by induction on m. First we must show that $n + 1 = 1 + n$ for all $n \in \mathbf{Z}^+$. Clearly $1 + 1 = 1 + 1$, and if $n + 1 = 1 + n$ then

$$
\begin{aligned}
s(n) + 1 &= (n + 1) + 1 &&\text{by A1} \\
&= (1 + n) + 1 \\
&= 1 + (n + 1) &&\text{by A2} \\
&= 1 + s(n) &&\text{by A1,}
\end{aligned}
$$

so that $n + 1 = 1 + n$ for all $n \in \mathbf{Z}^+$, by the principle of induction. Now suppose that $n + m = m + n$. By A1 and A2,

$$
n + s(m) = (m + n) + 1.
$$

---

[1] We do not mean to imply, by the use of the definite article 'the', that $n + m$ is uniquely determined by n and m, or even that this sum exists. In most of our definitions we refer to 'the (entity being defined)' and the same remarks apply. Such a definition is usually followed (or preceded, as it is here) by a proof of existence and uniqueness.

We have just shown that $n+1=1+n$ for all $n \in \mathbf{Z}^+$, so that

$$\begin{aligned} n + s(m) &= 1+(m+n) \\ &= (1+m)+n \\ &= s(m)+n, \end{aligned}$$

which proves (ii) by the principle of induction.

To prove (iii), we proceed by induction on n. It follows easily from (ii) and P2 that (iii) holds if $n=1$. Suppose that (iii) holds for n and that $s(n)+m=s(n)+r$. By (ii) and A2, $s(n+m)=s(n+r)$, so that $n+m=n+r$ by P2, and thus $m=r$. □

Property (i) above is called the *associative* law, (ii) is called the *commutative* or *abelian* law, and (iii) the *cancellation* law, so that Theorem 3 may be stated thus: *the addition of the positive integers is associative and commutative, and obeys the cancellation law.*

The product of two positive integers is defined in a similar way to the sum. First the existence and uniqueness of the product are proved.

THEOREM 4. *Let n be a positive integer. Then there is one and only one function f from* $\mathbf{Z}^+$ *to* $\mathbf{Z}^+$ *such that*:
M1: $f(1)=n$;
M2: $f(s(m))=f(m)+n$ *for all* $m \in \mathbf{Z}^+$.
The proof is similar to that of Theorem 2 and is left to the reader. Next the product is defined.

DEFINITION. The *product nm* of the positive integers n, m is the positive integer $f(m)$, where f is the function considered in Theorem 4.

We note that Theorem 4 is just the statement that nm exists and is uniquely determined by the ordered pair $\langle n, m \rangle$.

THEOREM 5. *If n, m, r are positive integers, then*:
(i) $n(m+r)=nm+nr$;
(ii) $(nm)r=n(mr)$;
(iii) $nm=mn$;
(iv) *if* $nm=nr$, *then* $m=r$.

The proofs of (i) and (ii) are quite straightforward. To prove (iii), first show that $(n+1)m=nm+m$ by induction on m, and then prove (iii) by induction on n. To prove (iv), first show that $n+m \neq n$ by generalizing Theorem 1(ii). Then prove (iv) by induction on m, using Theorem 1(i).

Properties (ii), (iii), and (iv) are called, respectively, the *associative*, *commutative* or *abelian*, and *cancellation* laws of multiplication, and (i) is the statement that the multiplication of the positive integers is *distributive* with respect to addition.

2

EXERCISES

1. Show that, for all positive integers n, $n + n = 2n$ and $n + (n + n) = 3n$.

2. Let c, d be positive integers such that $c \neq d$. Show that either there is a positive integer e such that $c + e = d$, or there is a positive integer f such that $c = d + f$.

4 The integers

For given positive integers a, b, there does not necessarily exist a positive integer c such that $a + c = b$. For example, by P1 there is no positive integer c such that $1 + c = 1$. Now we will embed $\mathbf{Z}^+$ in a set $\mathbf{Z}$, the set of all integers, in which $a + x = b$ can always be solved uniquely. The new elements – the negative integers and 0 – will be added to $\mathbf{Z}^+$ in rather a roundabout way: first we construct a new set from $\mathbf{Z}^+$, then we define appropriate operations of addition and multiplication on this new set, and finally we replace a subset of the new set by $\mathbf{Z}^+$.

Suppose, for the moment, that we have obtained such an extension of $\mathbf{Z}^+$. Since there is only one element c such that $a + c = b$ for given positive integers a, b, the element c is uniquely determined by the ordered pair $\langle a, b \rangle$. If two ordered pairs $\langle a, b \rangle$, $\langle d, e \rangle$ of positive integers are associated with c in this way, then, assuming that the usual laws of arithmetic hold, we have

$$a + e = a + (d + c) = (a + c) + d = b + d.$$

On the other hand, if a, b, d, e are positive integers such that $a + c = b$ and $a + e = b + d$, then

$$b + (d + c) = (b + d) + c = (e + a) + c = e + b,$$

so that $d + c = e$. Thus each element of the extension of $\mathbf{Z}^+$ is uniquely associated with a set of ordered pairs of positive integers, two such ordered pairs $\langle a, b \rangle$, $\langle d, e \rangle$ being in the same set if and only if $a + e = b + d$.

Now, motivated by the results in the preceding paragraph, we will construct the set of all integers from the set $\mathbf{Z}^+$. Consider the relation α defined on the set of all ordered pairs of positive integers by '$\langle a, b \rangle \; \alpha \; \langle d, e \rangle$ if and only if $a + e = b + d$'. This relation is easily seen to be an equivalence relation – the first two properties of an equivalence relation follow immediately from the commutativity of addition, and the third property is an easy consequence of the commutative, associative, and cancellation laws – so the set of all ordered pairs of positive integers has been partitioned into disjoint subsets, two ordered pairs $\langle a, b \rangle$, $\langle d, e \rangle$ being in the same subset if and only if $a + e = b + d$.

DEFINITION. An *integer* is an equivalence class determined by the relation α on the set of all ordered pairs of positive integers defined by '$\langle a, b \rangle \; \alpha \; \langle d, e \rangle$ if and only if $a + e = b + d$'. The set of integers is denoted by **Z**.

Using the notation of §1, an integer is denoted by a symbol like $[\langle a, b \rangle]$, where a, b are positive integers, meaning the set of all those ordered pairs $\langle d, e \rangle$ of positive integers such that $a + e = b + d$. This notation is obviously cumbersome, and integers will usually be denoted by lower case letters $a, b, c, \ldots$, as in Theorem 6 below.

DEFINITIONS. The *sum* $[\langle a, b \rangle] + [\langle d, e \rangle]$ of the integers $[\langle a, b \rangle]$, $[\langle d, e \rangle]$ is the integer $[\langle a + d, b + e \rangle]$, and their *product* $[\langle a, b \rangle] [\langle d, e \rangle]$ is the integer $[\langle ae + bd, be + ad \rangle]$. The integer $[\langle 1, 1 \rangle]$ is denoted by 0 and the integer $[\langle b, a \rangle]$ by $-[\langle a, b \rangle]$. The sum $n + (-m)$ of the integers n, $-m$ is denoted by $n - m$. Sometimes we will denote the product nm by $n \cdot m$.

Note how the sum $n + m$ of the integers n, m is found: elements $\langle a, b \rangle$, $\langle d, e \rangle$ are chosen arbitrarily from the integers n, m respectively, the ordered pair $\langle a + d, b + e \rangle$ is determined, and then the integer which contains this ordered pair is found. It might appear that $n + m$ depends not only on $\langle n, m \rangle$ but also on the particular elements which are chosen from n and m. Suppose that $\langle a, b \rangle$ and $\langle a', b' \rangle$ are in n and that $\langle d, e \rangle$ and $\langle d', e' \rangle$ are in m. Then $a + b' = b + a'$ and $d + e' = e + d'$, and an easy calculation shows that

$$(a + d) + (b' + e') = (b + e) + (a' + d'),$$

so that the integers $[\langle a + d, b + e \rangle]$, $[\langle a' + d', b' + e' \rangle]$ are the same. Similarly, the product nm of the integers n, m is uniquely determined by the ordered pair $\langle n, m \rangle$.

THEOREM 6. *If a, b, c are integers, then*:
(i) $(a + b) + c = a + (b + c)$;
(ii) $(ab)c = a(bc)$;
(iii) $a + b = b + a$;
(iv) $ab = ba$;
(v) $a + 0 = a$;
(vi) $a \cdot [\langle 1, 2 \rangle] = a$;
(vii) $a(b + c) = ab + ac$;
(viii) $a - a = 0$;
(ix) *if $ab = ac$ and $a \neq 0$, then $b = c$*;
(x) *there is one and only one integer x such that $a + x = b$; it is $b - a$.*

Proof. The various parts follow easily from the definitions and Theorems 3 and 5. For example, to prove (iii), let $a = [\langle d, e \rangle]$ and $b = [\langle f, g \rangle]$, where d, e, f, g are positive integers. Then $a + b = [\langle d + f, e + g \rangle]$ which, because $d + f = f + d$ and $e + g = g + e$, is $b + a$. To prove (x), use (i), (iii), and (viii) to show that $a + (b - a) = b$, and then, assuming that $a + x = b$, add $-a$ to both sides to obtain $x = b - a$. □

Properties (i)–(iv), (vii) and (ix) are referred to as the *associative, commutative* or *abelian, cancellation,* and *distributive* laws, just as were the analogous laws proved in Theorems 3 and 5.

Now we will replace certain of the integers by the original positive integers. Let a be a positive integer. It is certainly the solution to the equation $1 + x = 1 + a$, and this suggests that we replace $[\langle 1, 1 + a \rangle]$ by a. Note that a uniquely determines $[\langle 1, 1 + a \rangle]$. Also, every integer which is of the form $[\langle 1, 1 + a \rangle]$ uniquely determines the appropriate positive integer a, because if $[\langle 1, 1 + a \rangle] = [\langle 1, 1 + b \rangle]$, then $1 + (1 + a) = 1 + (1 + b)$, from which it follows that $a = b$. Thus we are assured that, when the replacement is carried out, every positive integer will replace an integer of the required type, and we will never discover, in attempting to insert a into the set of integers, that the integer it should replace has already been replaced by a different positive integer.

Now suppose that all the integers of the form $[\langle 1, 1 + a \rangle]$ have been replaced by the appropriate positive integers. We denote the resulting set by $\mathbf{Z}'$. Thus, an element of $\mathbf{Z}'$ is either a positive integer, or else an integer which is not of the form $[\langle 1, 1 + a \rangle]$. We define the *sum* and *product* of any two elements of $\mathbf{Z}'$ to be the sum and product which would be obtained if the replacement had never taken place. That is, for purposes of calculation, the positive integer a is treated as if it were the integer $[\langle 1, 1 + a \rangle]$. Obviously, Theorem 6 still applies, but we now have two meanings for the sum and product of two positive integers: they can be found either by taking the positive integers simply as positive integers and using the definitions of §3, or else by regarding the positive integers as elements of $\mathbf{Z}'$ and determining their sum and product as in this section. The result is the same in either case: if a, b are positive integers then their sum, calculated as if they were elements of $\mathbf{Z}'$, is $[\langle 1, 1 + a \rangle] + [\langle 1, 1 + b \rangle] = [\langle 2, 2 + (a + b) \rangle]$, which is $[\langle 1, 1 + (a + b) \rangle]$, and this has been replaced by $a + b$. Similarly, their product would be $[\langle 1, 1 + ab \rangle]$, and this has been replaced by ab.

Now we have achieved the objective of this section – the set of positive integers has been embedded in a set in which $a + x = b$ is always solvable. Henceforth, by the term *positive integer* we shall mean either an element of the original set of positive integers as defined in §2 or an integer of the form $[\langle 1, 1 + a \rangle]$, and regard a and $[\langle 1, 1 + a \rangle]$ as the same, even writing $a = [\langle 1, 1 + a \rangle]$ as in the proof of the next theorem. We have just seen that this will not lead to any ambiguity. Also, the symbol $\mathbf{Z}$ will be used both for $\mathbf{Z}$ as previously defined and for $\mathbf{Z}'$, since there is no longer any distinction between a and $[\langle 1, 1 + a \rangle]$.

In Chapter 2 we will embed the set of integers in the set of rational numbers, the set of rational numbers in the set of real numbers, and the set of real numbers in the set of complex numbers, and in Chapter 3 we will consider the embedding of one set in another in a very general context, so it is worth noting here the essential features of our embedding of $\mathbf{Z}^+$ in $\mathbf{Z}$. We began by associating a with $[\langle 1, 1 + a \rangle]$. That is, we considered the function defined by

$$f(a) = [\langle 1, 1 + a \rangle],$$

and we proved that:

(i) f is an injection: a given integer is not replaced by two different positive integers;

(ii) $f(a + b) = f(a) + f(b)$ and $f(ab) = f(a) f(b)$ for all a, $b \in \mathbf{Z}^+$: $a + b$ and $f(a) + f(b)$ are the same integer and ab and $f(a) f(b)$ are the same integer.

These properties of f were sufficient to ensure that $\mathbf{Z}^+$ could be embedded in $\mathbf{Z}$. In Chapter 3 we shall call a function with these properties an *injective homomorphism* from the *ring* $\mathbf{Z}^+$ to the *ring* $\mathbf{Z}$.

DEFINITIONS. An integer a is *negative* if $-a$ is positive. If a, b are integers and $a - b$ is positive, then a is *greater than* b, and this is denoted by $a > b$. By b is *less than* a, denoted by $b < a$, we mean that a is greater than b. If $a > b$ or $a = b$, then this is denoted by $a \geqslant b$ or by $b \leqslant a$.

THEOREM 7. *If a, b are integers, then either $a > b$, $a < b$, or $a = b$. If $a \leqslant b$ and $a \geqslant b$, then $a = b$.*

Proof. (i) First we show that, if c, d are positive integers and $c \neq d$, then either there is a positive integer e such that $c + e = d$ or there is a positive integer f such that $c = d + f$. (This was set as Exercise 2 on p. 10.) Fixing the positive integer c, we show by induction on d that either (a) $c + e = d$ for some $e \in \mathbf{Z}^+$; or (b) $c = d$; or (c) $c = d + f$ for some $f \in \mathbf{Z}^+$.

We must first show that one of these three statements holds if $d = 1$. If $c = 1$, then (b) holds. If $c \neq 1$, then $c = 1 + f$ for some $f \in \mathbf{Z}^+$, by Theorem 1(i), and (c) holds.

Now suppose that d satisfies one of (a), (b), (c). We must show that either (d) $c + g = d + 1$ for some $g \in \mathbf{Z}^+$; or (e) $c = d + 1$; or (f) $c = (d + 1) + h$

for some $h \in \mathbf{Z}^+$. If (a) holds, then $c + (e + 1) = d + 1$, so (d) holds. If (b) holds, then $c + 1 = d + 1$ and (d) holds. If (c) holds and $c \neq d + 1$, then $c = d + f$ and $f \neq 1$. By Theorem 1(i), there is a positive integer h such that $f = h + 1$. Clearly, $c = (d + 1) + h$, and thus (f) holds.

We have now shown, by the principle of induction, that at least one of (a), (b), (c) holds, for $c, d \in \mathbf{Z}^+$.

(ii) Let c, d be positive integers, and consider the integer $a = [\langle c, d \rangle]$. If $a \neq 0$ then $c \neq d$, so either there is a positive integer e such that $c + e = d$ or there is a positive integer f such that $c = d + f$. In the first case,

$$a = [\langle c, c + e \rangle] = [\langle 1, 1 + e \rangle] = e,$$

so that a is a positive integer. In the second case,

$$-a = [\langle d, c \rangle] = [\langle d, d + f \rangle] = [\langle 1, 1 + f \rangle] = f,$$

so that $-a$ is positive, and therefore a is negative.

(iii) Now let a, b be any integers. If $a \neq b$, then $a - b \neq 0$, so, by (ii), one of $a - b, -(a - b)$ is positive. If $a - b$ is positive, then $a > b$. If $-(a - b)$ is positive, then, since $-(a - b) = b - a$, as follows easily from Theorem 6, we have $b > a$. We have now proved the first part of the theorem.

(iv) Suppose that $a \leqslant b$, $b \leqslant a$, and $a \neq b$. Then both $b - a$ and $a - b$ are positive integers. Since the sum of any two positive integers is a positive integer, 0 must be positive. Thus there must be a positive integer d such that

$$0 = [\langle 1, 1 \rangle] = [\langle 1, 1 + d \rangle].$$

But this implies that $1 + d = 1$, and this is impossible by P1. $\square$

The remaining properties of the relation of inequality are considerably easier to prove than Theorem 7, and are left as exercises.

EXERCISES

1. Prove that, for all integers a, b:
(i) $-(-a) = a$; (ii) $0a = 0$; (iii) $a(-b) = -(ab)$; (iv) $(-a)(-b) = ab$; (v) $2a \neq 1$.

2. Show that, if a, b, c are integers such that $a + b = a + c$, then $b = c$.

3. Let g be an injection from $\mathbf{Z}^+$ to $\mathbf{Z}$ such that $g(a + b) = g(a) + g(b)$ and $g(ab) = g(a) g(b)$ for all $a, b \in \mathbf{Z}^+$. Show that $g(a) = [\langle 1, 1 + a \rangle]$ for all $a \in \mathbf{Z}^+$.

4. Show that, for all integers a, b, c:
(i) a is positive if and only if $a > 0$;
(ii) $0 < a < 1$ cannot hold;
(iii) if $b < a + 1$, then $b \leqslant a$;
(iv) if $a < b$, then $a + c < b + c$;

(v) if $a < b$ and c is positive, then $ac < bc$;
(vi) if $a < b$ and $b < c$, then $a < c$.

5. For every integer a, define the *absolute value* of a, denoted by $|a|$, to be a if $a \geqslant 0$ and $-a$ if $a < 0$. Show that, for all integers a, b:

(i) $|ab| = |a|\,|b|$ and $|a + b| \leqslant |a| + |b|$;
(ii) if $a \neq 0$, then $|a| \geqslant 1$;
(iii) if $|a| < b$, then $-b < a < b$.

5   The well-ordering of the positive integers

The properties of the relation of inequality which we considered in the last section will all be extended later to the rational numbers and the real numbers. In this section we prove a result which cannot be so extended, a result which we later show characterizes the positive integers.

DEFINITION. An integer a is the *least* or *smallest* member of a set A of integers if $a \in A$ and, whenever $b < a$, then $b \notin A$.

For example, 1 is the least member of $\mathbf{Z}^+$, whereas there is no least member of $\mathbf{Z}$.

We have referred to *the* least member of a set in the definition; it is easy to see that a set A cannot have two least members. Suppose that a, c are the least members of a set A of integers. Then $a \leqslant c$, because $c \in A$ and a is the least member of A. Similarly $c \leqslant a$, so that $a = c$.

THEOREM 8 (*The Well-Ordering Theorem for the Positive Integers*). *Every non-empty set of positive integers has a least member.*

Proof. Suppose that A is a set of positive integers which has no least member. We will show that A is empty, and thus prove the theorem. Let

$$B = \{x \mid x < c \text{ for all } c \in A\}.$$

Note that if $b \in B$ then $b \notin A$. Thus in order to show that A is empty it is sufficient to show that every positive integer is in B. We will prove this by induction.

(i) If $1 \notin B$, then there must be an integer $c \leqslant 1$ such that $c \in A$. Since the integers in A are positive, $c = 1$, so that $1 \in A$, and A accordingly has a least member 1. This is contrary to our assumption, so $1 \in B$.

(ii) Suppose that $b \in B$ and that $c \leqslant b + 1$. To show that $b + 1 \in B$ we must show that $c \notin A$. If $c = b + 1$ and $c \in A$, then c is the least member of A; and this, by our assumption, is impossible. If $c < b + 1$ then $c \leqslant b$, and thus, because $b \in B$, $c \notin A$.

Thus, by the principle of induction, every positive integer is in B, and this, by our previous remarks, proves the theorem. □

DEFINITIONS. An integer a is the *largest* or *greatest* member of a set A of integers if $a \in A$ and if, whenever $b > a$, then $b \notin A$. An integer c is an *upper bound* for A if $d \leqslant c$ for all $d \in A$; c is a *lower bound* for A if $d \geqslant c$ for all $d \in A$. If A has an upper bound then A is *bounded above*. If A has a lower bound then A is *bounded below*.

With these new terms we now apply Theorem 8 to obtain similar results for sets of integers:

(i) *If a non-empty set A of integers is bounded below, then it has a least member.*

Proof. Let c be a lower bound for A and let B be the set of all integers of the form $(a+1) - c$, where $a \in A$. B is non-empty and its members are positive, so B has a least member d. The integer $(d+c) - 1$ is easily seen to be the least member of A. □

(ii) *If a non-empty set A of integers is bounded above, then it has a greatest member.*

Proof. Let B be the set of all integers of the form $-a$, where $a \in A$. By (i), B has a least member d; and $-d$ is easily seen to be the greatest member of A. □

EXERCISES

1. Show that a set of integers cannot have two largest members.

2. Let A be a non-empty set of integers which is bounded above, and let B be the set of all upper bounds of A. Show that the least member of B is the largest member of A. State and prove a similar result for the case in which A is bounded below.

3. Let A be a non-empty set of positive integers with the property that, if $a \in A$ and $a \neq 1$, then there is a $b \in A$ such that $b < a$. Show that $1 \in A$.

4. Let A be a non-empty set of positive integers with the property that, if b is a positive integer and $a \in A$ for all positive integers a less than b, then $b \in A$. Show that every positive integer is in A.

5. Let A be a set of positive integers with the properties:
(i) If n is a positive integer, then there is an integer $m > n$ such that $m \in A$;
(ii) If n is a positive integer and $1 + n \in A$, then $n \in A$.
Show that every positive integer is in A.

6   The number of elements in a set

DEFINITIONS. If a, b are integers, then the set $\{x \mid a \leqslant x \leqslant b\}$ is denoted by $]a, b[$. A set A *contains exactly a elements*, or a is the *number of elements* in A, if $a \geqslant 1$ and there is a bijection from $]1, a[$ to A. If A is empty, it *contains exactly* 0 *elements*. If A contains exactly a elements for some a, then A is *finite*. If A is not finite it is *infinite*.

If A contains exactly a elements, then these elements can be counted off as $f(1), f(2), \ldots, f(a)$, where f is a suitable bijection. We note that f is unique only if $a = 1$ – if $a > 1$, then A can be counted off in several different ways. For example, if $a = 2$ then there are 2 possible bijections, and if $a = 3$ then there are 6 possible bijections. Thus it is not at all obvious that if a set is finite then the number of elements in it is unique. This is proved in the next theorem.

THEOREM 9. (i) *If* A, B *are sets such that* $B \subseteq A$ *and* A, B *contain the same number of elements, then* $A = B$.
(ii) *If* A *contains exactly* a *elements, then* a *is uniquely determined by* A.
(iii) *The set of all positive integers is infinite.*

Proof. (i) We proceed by induction on the number of elements in A and B. If A, B are empty or contain exactly 1 element, and $B \subseteq A$, then it is easy to see that $A = B$. Suppose that a is a positive integer with the property that, if A, B are sets, each containing a elements, and $B \subseteq A$, then $A = B$. Let A', B' be sets, each containing exactly $a + 1$ elements, and such that $B' \subseteq A'$. To prove (i) we must show that $A' = B'$.

Let f, g be bijections from $]1, a+1[$ to A', B' respectively, and let b be that integer in $]1, a+1[$ such that $g(a+1) = f(b)$. Let A, B be A', B' with $f(b)$ deleted, and let f', g' be the functions, from $]1, a[$ to A, B respectively, defined by:

$$f'(c) = \begin{cases} f(c) & \text{if } 1 \leqslant c < b \\ f(c+1) & \text{if } b \leqslant c \leqslant a; \end{cases}$$

$$g'(c) = g(c) \qquad \text{if } 1 \leqslant c \leqslant a.$$

It is easy to see that f' and g' are bijections, so that A and B both contain exactly a elements. Also, $B \subseteq A$, so that $A = B$. But A', B' are just A, B with $f(b)$ adjoined, so $A' = B'$.

(ii) If A is empty, then a must be 0. Suppose that A is not empty, that it contains exactly a elements and exactly b elements, and that $a \leqslant b$. Let f be a bijection from $]1, b[$ to A, and let B be the set of those elements in A which are of the form $f(c)$ for some $c \in]1, a[$. (In the notation of Exercise 5, p. 4, $B = f(]1, a[)$.) Let g be the function from $]1, a[$ to B defined by

$$g(c) = f(c) \text{ for all } c \in]1, a[.$$

Then g is a bijection, so B contains exactly a elements. By (i), $B = A$, and therefore $a = b$. Similarly if $a \geqslant b$, then $a = b$.

(iii) If $\mathbf{Z}^+$ contains exactly a elements for some integer a, then, because

]1, a[also contains exactly a elements,]1, a[is $\mathbf{Z}^+$ by (i). This is not the case, since $a+1$, for example, is a positive integer which is not in]1, a[. $\square$

EXERCISES

1. Show that, if A contains exactly a elements and $C \subseteq A$, then C contains exactly c elements for some $c \in {]0, a[}$.

2. Show that a set A is infinite if and only if there is a set $B \subseteq A$ such that $B \neq A$ and a bijection from A to B.

3. Show that, if A, B are disjoint sets containing exactly a, b elements respectively, then $A \cup B$ contains exactly $a + b$ elements.

4. Let a be an integer and let f be a surjection from]1, a[to a set A. Show that there is an integer b such that $b \leqslant a$ and A contains exactly b elements.

7 The general associative and commutative laws

DEFINITIONS. An *infinite sequence* of elements of a set A is a function from the set of positive integers to A. A *finite sequence* of elements of A is a function from]1, n[to A, where n is a positive integer. If f is a sequence, then $f(i)$ is called the *i-th term* of f and usually denoted by f_i. An infinite sequence f will usually be denoted by $(f_i)_i$, or by

$$f_1, f_2, f_3, \ldots,$$

and a finite sequence f from]1, n[to A by

$$f_1, f_2, f_3, \ldots, f_n.$$

For example, 1, 1, 2, and 2, 1, 1, are finite sequences of integers, and the function defined by $f(i) = 2i$ is an infinite sequence of integers which we would denote by $(2i)_i$ or by

$$2, 4, 6, \ldots.$$

Whenever we refer to 'the elements $f_1, f_2, f_3, \ldots, f_n$ of a set A', it should be understood that we are really referring to a finite sequence of elements of A.

THEOREM 10. *If $(a_i)_i$ is an infinite sequence of integers, then there is one and only one infinite sequence of integers $(b_i)_i$ such that $b_1 = a_1$ and $b_i = b_{i-1} + a_i$ for all $i > 1$, and there is one and only one sequence of integers $(c_i)_i$ such that $c_1 = a_1$ and $c_i = c_{i-1} a_i$ for all $i > 1$. Also, b_i and c_i depend only on the finite sequence $a_1, a_2, a_3, \ldots, a_i$.*

Proof. First we show that, for every $n \in \mathbf{Z}^+$, there is a finite sequence f_n from]1, n[to $\mathbf{Z}$ such that $f_n(1) = a_1$ and $f_n(i) = f_n(i-1) + a_i$ for all $i \in {]2, n[}$. This is easily proved by induction: the finite sequence a_1 can be associated with $n = 1$; and if f_n exists, then a suitable sequence f_{n+1} is defined by

$$f_{n+1}(i) = \begin{cases} f_n(i) & \text{for } i \in \,]1, n[\\ f_n(n) + a_{n+1} & \text{for } i = n+1. \end{cases}$$

Now we show that, for all $i > 1$,

$$f_i(j) = f_j(j)$$

for all $j \in \,]1, i[$. If this is not the case then, by Theorem 8, there is a smallest integer i for which $f_i(j) \neq f_j(j)$ for some $j \in \,]1, i[$. Let this smallest integer be n, and let the smallest integer j such that $j \in \,]1, n[$ and $f_n(j) \neq f_j(j)$ be m. Since $f_i(1) = f_1(1)$ for all i, m must be greater than 1, so f_{m-1} is defined. From the choice of m,

$$f_n(m-1) = f_{m-1}(m-1).$$

Obviously $m < n$, so, by the choice of n,

$$f_m(j) = f_j(j)$$

for all $j \in \,]1, m[$, and in particular for $j = m - 1$. Thus

$$\begin{aligned} f_n(m) &= f_n(m-1) + a_m \\ &= f_{m-1}(m-1) + a_m \\ &= f_m(m-1) + a_m \\ &= f_m(m). \end{aligned}$$

This contradicts the choice of n and m, and thus proves the required result.

Now let $(b_i)_i$ be the infinite sequence whose i-th term is $f_i(i)$. Obviously $b_1 = a_1$, and

$$\begin{aligned} b_i &= f_i(i) \\ &= f_i(i-1) + a_i \\ &= f_{i-1}(i-1) + a_i \\ &= b_{i-1} + a_i \end{aligned}$$

for all $i > 1$, by the definitions and the preceding result.

To show that $(b_i)_i$ is uniquely determined by the given conditions, suppose that $(d_i)_i$ is another such sequence. By Theorem 8, there is a smallest integer n such that $b_n \neq d_n$. Since $b_1 = d_1 = a_1$, n must be greater than 1, so that b_{n-1}, d_{n-1} are defined and equal. But

$$b_n = b_{n-1} + a_n = d_{n-1} + a_n = d_n,$$

and this contradicts the choice of n. To show that b_i depends only on the finite sequence $a_1, a_2, a_3, \ldots, a_i$, note that this is true if $i = 1$, and if it is true for $i = n$ then, since b_{n+1} is determined by b_n and a_{n+1}, it is true for $i = n + 1$.

The proof of the remainder of the theorem is similar to the above, addition being replaced by multiplication. $\square$

In the above proof the uniqueness of the sequence $(b_i)_i$ could obviously be proved by induction rather than by the use of Theorem 8, but it is not so easy to show that $f_i(j) = f_j(j)$ by induction. Any result which is proved by induction can also be proved using Theorem 8: if the result does not hold, then there is a smallest integer n for which it does not hold, and a contradiction is obtained from the existence of n by arguments similar to those used in the induction proof.

DEFINITIONS. Let $(a_i)_i$ be an infinite sequence of integers. If $(b_i)_i$ is an infinite sequence of integers such that $b_1 = a_1$ and $b_i = b_{i-1} + a_i$ for all $i > 1$, then b_n is the *sum of the finite sequence* $a_1, a_2, a_3, \ldots, a_n$, and is denoted by $\sum_{i=1}^{n} a_i$ or by $a_1 + a_2 + a_3 + \ldots + a_n$. If $(c_i)_i$ is an infinite sequence of integers such that $c_1 = a_1$ and $c_i = c_{i-1} a_i$ for all $i > 1$, then c_n is the *product of the finite sequence* $a_1, a_2, a_3, \ldots, a_n$, and is denoted by $\prod_{i=1}^{n} a_i$ or by $a_1 a_2 a_3 \ldots a_n$. If $1 < m \leqslant n$, then $\sum_{i=1}^{n+1-m} a_{m+i-1}$ is denoted by $\sum_{i=m}^{n} a_i$ and $\prod_{i=1}^{n+1-m} a_{m+i-1}$ by $\prod_{i=m}^{n} a_i$. If all the terms of $(a_i)_i$ are the same, say a, then $\prod_{i=1}^{n} a_i$ is denoted by a^n.

Theorem 10 states that $\sum_{i=1}^{n} a_i$ and $\prod_{i=1}^{n} a_i$ exist, and are uniquely determined by the finite sequence $a_1, a_2, a_3, \ldots, a_n$.

Note that the associative laws of addition and multiplication were not used in the proof of Theorem 10. This is because we have formed the sums and products in a particular way, for example,

$$\sum_{i=1}^{3} a_i = (a_1 + a_2) + a_3$$

and
$$\sum_{i=1}^{4} a_i = ((a_1 + a_2) + a_3) + a_4.$$

By the associative law of addition,

$$\sum_{i=1}^{3} a_i = a_1 + (a_2 + a_3) = \sum_{i=1}^{1} a_i + \sum_{i=2}^{3} a_i$$

and similarly, for all integers s such that $1 \leqslant s < 4$,

$$\sum_{i=1}^{4} a_i = \sum_{i=1}^{s} a_i + \sum_{i=s+1}^{4} a_i.$$

The next theorem generalizes these associative laws in an obvious way.

THEOREM 11 (*The General Associative Law of Addition of Integers*). *If $(a_i)_i$ is an infinite sequence of integers, and s, n are integers such that $1 \leqslant s < n$, then*

$$\sum_{i=1}^{n} a_i = \sum_{i=1}^{s} a_i + \sum_{i=s+1}^{n} a_i.$$

Proof. We proceed by induction on n. The statement of the theorem certainly holds if $n = 1$. Suppose it holds if $n = m$, and let s be an integer such that $1 \leqslant s < m + 1$. There are two cases to consider:
(i) If $s = m$, then, by the definition of sum,

$$\sum_{i=1}^{m+1} a_i = \sum_{i=1}^{s} a_i + a_{m+1},$$

which is the required result.
(ii) If $1 \leqslant s < m$, then

$$\begin{aligned}
\sum_{i=1}^{m+1} a_i &= \sum_{i=1}^{m} a_i + a_{m+1} \\
&= \left(\sum_{i=1}^{s} a_i + \sum_{i=s+1}^{m} a_i \right) + a_{m+1} \\
&= \sum_{i=1}^{s} a_i + \left(\sum_{i=s+1}^{m} a_i + a_{m+1} \right) \\
&= \sum_{i=1}^{s} a_i + \sum_{i=s+1}^{m+1} a_i.
\end{aligned}$$

Thus, if the theorem holds for $n = m$ then it holds for $n = m + 1$, so, by the principle of induction, it holds for all n. □

Note that in case (ii) of the above proof we used the special case $n = 3$, which was proved in Theorem 6(i). This, perhaps, was expected by the reader, because if the special case had not been required then there would have been no necessity for proving it separately. It would have followed from Theorem 11. Usually, if a theorem is generalized by an induction argument then it must be used in the proof, and often the theorem is the first non-trivial case of the more general result as it was here – Theorem 11 is trivial if $n = 1$ or 2.

We now generalize the commutative law of addition by showing that $\sum_{i=1}^{n} a_i$ is independent of the order of the terms. Consider what this means if $n = 2$. We have shown that

$$a_1 + a_2 = a_2 + a_1$$

for all integers a_1, a_2 (and so, incidentally, we expect to use this result in the proof of its generalization). The sum $a_1 + a_2$ is $\sum_{i=1}^{2} a_i$, and $a_2 + a_1$ is $\sum_{i=1}^{2} a_{g(i)}$, where g is the bijection from $]1, 2[$ to $]1, 2[$ defined by $g(1) = 2$ and $g(2) = 1$.

There are only two bijections from $]1, 2[$ to $]1, 2[$, the other one being defined by $g(1) = 1, g(2) = 2$. Thus

$$\sum_{i=1}^{2} a_i = \sum_{i=1}^{2} a_{g(i)}$$

for any infinite sequence of integers a_1, a_2, a_3,..., and any bijection g from $]1, 2[$ to $]1, 2[$.

THEOREM 12 (*The General Commutative Law of Addition of Integers*). *If $(a_i)_i$ is an infinite sequence of integers, n a positive integer, and g a bijection from $]1, n[$ to $]1, n[$, then*

$$\sum_{i=1}^{n} a_i = \sum_{i=1}^{n} a_{g(i)}.$$

Proof. We proceed by induction on n. Clearly, the statement of the theorem holds if $n = 1$. Suppose it holds if $n = m$, and let g be a bijection from $]1, m+1[$ to $]1, m+1[$. We now modify g in much the same way as we modified f and g in Theorem 9(i). Let s be that integer in $]1, m+1[$ for which $g(s) = m+1$, and let g' be the function from $]1, m[$ to $]1, m[$ defined by

$$g'(i) = \begin{cases} g(i) & \text{if } i < s \\ g(i+1) & \text{if } i \geqslant s. \end{cases}$$

Then g' is a bijection from $]1, m[$ to $]1, m[$, so that

$$\sum_{i=1}^{m} a_i = \sum_{i=1}^{m} a_{g'(i)}.$$

Suppose that $1 < s < m+1$. Then, by Theorem 11,

$$\sum_{i=1}^{m+1} a_{g(i)} = \left(\sum_{i=1}^{s-1} a_{g(i)} + a_{g(s)} \right) + \sum_{i=s+1}^{m+1} a_{g(i)}.$$

By Theorem 6(i), (iii), the definitions of g' and s, and Theorem 11,

$$\sum_{i=1}^{m+1} a_{g(i)} = \sum_{i=1}^{m} a_{g'(i)} + a_{m+1};$$

and since the statement of the theorem holds for $n = m$, this is $\sum_{i=1}^{m+1} a_i$.

If $s = 1$ or $s = m+1$, then the same relation is shown to hold by omitting the appropriate sums from the above equations. Thus, by the principle of induction, the proof is complete. $\square$

The proof of the next theorem is similar to the proofs of Theorems 11 and 12, addition being replaced by multiplication.

THEOREM 13 (*The General Associative and Commutative Laws of Multiplication of Integers*). *If* $(a_i)_i$ *is an infinite sequence of integers, and s, n are integers such that $1 \leqslant s < n$, then*

$$\prod_{i=1}^{n} a_i = \left(\prod_{i=1}^{s} a_i \right) \left(\prod_{i=s+1}^{n} a_i \right).$$

If g is a bijection from $]1, n[$ to $]1, n[$, then

$$\prod_{i=1}^{n} a_i = \prod_{i=1}^{n} a_{g(i)}.$$

EXERCISES

1. Let a be an integer and let n, m be positive integers. Show that,

(i) $\sum_{i=1}^{n} a = na$;

(ii) $(a^n)(a^m) = a^{n+m}$;

(iii) $(a^n)^m = a^{nm}$.

2. Prove by induction that, for all positive integers n, $\sum_{i=1}^{n} 2i = n(n+1)$.

3. Let $(a_i)_i$ be an infinite sequence of integers such that $a_i \geqslant a_1$ for all i. Show that $\sum_{i=1}^{n} a_i \geqslant na_1$ for all positive integers n.

4. Show that, if g is an injection from $]1, n[$ to $]1, n[$, then g is a bijection.

5. Show that, if $(a_i)_i$ is an infinite sequence of integers such that $a_{n+1} = a_n$ for all n, then $a_n = a_1$.

6. Prove Theorem 13 using Theorem 8 instead of the principle of induction.

7. Show that, if $a_1, a_2, a_3, \ldots, a_{n+1}$ is a finite sequence of integers, then there is a bijection g from $]1, n+1[$ to $]1, n+1[$ such that $a_{g(i)} \leqslant a_{g(i+1)}$ for all $i \in]1, n[$.

8. Let $A_1, A_2, A_3, \ldots, A_m$ be a finite sequence of pairwise-disjoint sets, A_i containing exactly n_i elements for each i. Show that the union of these sets contains exactly $\sum_{i=1}^{m} n_i$ elements.

9. Show that, for all integers a, b, and all integers $n \geqslant 3$,

$$a^n - b^n = (a - b) \left(\sum_{i=1}^{n-2} a^i b^{n-i-1} + a^{n-1} + b^{n-1} \right).$$

10. Let the relation α on $\mathbf{Z}$ be defined by '$a \, \alpha \, b$ if and only if either '$a = b$ or, for some positive integer n, $a = b2^n$ or $b = a2^n$'. Show that α is an equivalence relation on $\mathbf{Z}$, and that there are integers a, b, such that $[a+b]$ is not uniquely determined by $[a]$ and $[b]$.

11. Prove the *Dirichlet box principle*: If $n+1$ things are distributed among n boxes, then some box contains at least two things.

12. Let B be a set of n boys and let G be a set of girls. In order that every boy in B can marry an acquaintance in G it is obviously necessary that, for every subset P of B, the boys in P know, collectively, as many girls in G as there are boys in P. Show that this condition is also sufficient.

8 Divisibility

THEOREM 14 (*The Division Theorem*). *If a, b are integers and $b \neq 0$, then there are unique integers q, r such that $a = bq + r$ and $0 \leqslant r < |b|$.*[1]

Proof. The method of proof is suggested by noting that the required integer r will be the smallest integer which is $\geqslant 0$ and is of the form $a - bq$ for some integer q. Therefore, consider the set

$$A = \{x \mid x \text{ is an integer}, x \geqslant 0, \text{ and } x = a + bn \text{ for some integer } n\}.$$

To show that A is not empty, note that

$$a + |b||a| \geqslant a + |a| \geqslant 0,$$

so that $a + bn$ is in A, where $n = |a|$ if $b > 0$ and $n = -|a|$ if $b < 0$. Clearly, A is bounded below by 0. Thus A contains a least integer r. Since $r \in A$, $r \geqslant 0$, and there is an integer q such that $a = bq + r$. Suppose that $r \geqslant |b|$. Then $r - |b| \geqslant 0$, and $r - |b| = a - b(q \pm 1)$, so that $r - |b| \in A$. But r is the least integer in A, so that $r \leqslant r - |b|$, and this is impossible. Therefore $r < |b|$.

To complete the proof we must show that q, r are unique. Suppose that s, t are integers such that $a = bs + t$ and $0 \leqslant t < |b|$. Then $b(s - q) = r - t$, so that, if $s \neq q$, we would have $|r - t| \geqslant |b|$. This is impossible because $0 \leqslant t < |b|$ and $0 \leqslant r < |b|$. Thus $s = q$ and, because $r - t = b(s - q)$, therefore $r = t$. □

DEFINITION. If a, b are integers, then b *divides* a or is a *divisor* of a if there is an integer c such that $a = bc$. If b divides a, we write $b \mid a$.

We note that:

(i) $a \mid a$ for every integer a;
(ii) $a \mid 0$ for every integer a;
(iii) if $0 \mid a$, then $a = 0$;
(iv) if $a \mid b$ and $b \mid c$, then $a \mid c$;
(v) if $a \mid b$ and $b \neq 0$, then $0 < |a| \leqslant |b|$;
(vi) if $a \mid b$ and $a \mid c$, then $a \mid sb + tc$ for all integers s, t.

---

[1] q is called the *quotient* and r the *remainder* obtained when b is divided into a.

Any two integers a, b have a common divisor, 1, and if $a \neq 0$ and $c \mid a$ then, by (v) above, $c \leqslant |a|$. Thus, if at least one of a, b is not 0, then the set of common divisors of a and b is not empty and is bounded above. Therefore there is a *greatest common divisor* of a and b, which is uniquely determined by a and b. It will be denoted by (a, b).

To find the greatest common divisor of two integers we can use the procedure known as *Euclid's Algorithm*: Let a, b be integers, $b \neq 0$. By the division theorem, there are integers q, r such that $a = bq + r$ and $0 \leqslant r < |b|$. If c is a common divisor of a and b then, by (vi) above, $c \mid r$, so c is a common divisor of b and r. Similarly, every common divisor of b and r is a common divisor of a and b. Thus $(a, b) = (b, r)$. If $r = 0$ then $b \mid a$, so that $(a, b) = |b|$. If $r \neq 0$ then there are integers q_1, r_1 such that $b = rq_1 + r_1$ and $0 \leqslant r_1 < r$. As before, $(b, r) = (r, r_1)$, so that $(a, b) = (r, r_1)$. If $r_1 = 0$ then $(a, b) = r$, and if $r_1 \neq 0$ the procedure is to be repeated. Continuing in this way, we find integers $r, r_1, r_2, \ldots, q, q_1, q_2, \ldots$, such that

$$a = bq + r,$$
$$b = rq_1 + r_1,$$
$$r = r_1 q_2 + r_2,$$
$$r_1 = r_2 q_3 + r_3,$$
$$\cdots\cdots\cdots\cdots$$

the procedure ending when a 0 remainder is achieved. This must happen after a finite number of steps, since

$$r > r_1 > r_2 > \ldots > 0;$$

and, by the above, (a, b) is the last non-0 remainder.

Since Euclid's algorithm will not be used in any subsequent proof the formal details are omitted. Obviously, a phrase like 'continuing in this way' must be elaborated, and we have omitted the proof that the remainder must eventually be 0.

DEFINITION. An integer c is a *linear combination* of the integers a, b if there are integers s, t such that $c = sa + tb$.

THEOREM 15. *Let a, b be integers, not both 0. Then*:

(i) (a, b) *is a linear combination of* a, b;
(ii) *if $c \mid a$ and $c \mid b$, then $c \mid (a, b)$.*

Proof. Suppose that (i) does not hold, and that $b \neq 0$. Consider the following set A of positive integers:

$$A = \{c \mid c \in \mathbf{Z}^+ \text{ and, for some } n \in \mathbf{Z}, (c,n) \text{ is not a linear combination of } c \text{ and } n\}.$$

3

Then A is not empty, since one of b, $-b$ is in A; and A is obviously bounded below. Let d be the least member of A and let n be an integer such that (d,n) is not a linear combination of d and n. Since $d > 0$, there are integers q, r such that $n = dq+r$ and $0 \leqslant r < d$. By the argument used in the discussion of Euclid's algorithm, $(d,n) = (d,r)$. If $r = 0$, then $(d,n) = (d,r) = d$, which is a linear combination of d and n. Thus $r > 0$, so r is a positive integer which is not in A. Therefore (d,r) is a linear combination of d and r, so that (d,n) is a linear combination of d and r. But r is a linear combination of d and n, so (d,n) is a linear combination of d and n. This contradicts the definition of n, and proves (i).

Part (ii) follows immediately from (i) and the fact that, if $c\,|\,a$ and $c\,|\,b$, then c divides every linear combination of a and b. $\square$

In practice, (a, b) is expressed as a linear combination of a and b by applying Euclid's algorithm to find (a, b), and then using the resulting equations in the reverse order to find the linear combination.

EXAMPLE. Suppose that we wish to find $(40, 14)$ as a linear combination of 40 and 14. Applying the algorithm, we have

$$40 = 14 \cdot 2 + 12$$
$$14 = 12 \cdot 1 + 2$$
$$12 = 6 \cdot 2 + 0,$$

so that $(40, 14) = 2$. Now we express the 12 in the second equation as a linear combination of 40 and 14 from the first equation and obtain

$$2 = 14 - (40 - 14 \cdot 2)$$
$$= 3 \cdot 14 + -1 \cdot 40.$$

Note that 2 is not uniquely expressed as a linear combination of 14 and 40; for example, we also have

$$2 = -17 \cdot 14 + 6 \cdot 40.$$

EXERCISES

1. Find $(186, 42)$ and $(15, 77)$ by Euclid's algorithm, and express them as appropriate linear combinations.

2. Show that, if a, b, c are integers and $a \neq 0$, then:
(i) if $c > 0$, then $(ca, cb) = c \cdot (a, b)$;
(ii) if $(a, b) = (a, c) = 1$, then $(a, bc) = 1$;
(iii) if $a\,|\,b$ and $c\,|\,b$, then $ac\,|\,b \cdot (a, c)$.

3. Show that the smallest positive linear combination of two integers a, b, which are not both 0, is (a, b).

4. A set I of integers is called an *ideal* if it is not empty and

(i) $a + b \in I$ if $a \in I$ and $b \in I$;

(ii) $ac \in I$ if $a \in I$ and c is an integer.

Show that if I is an ideal, then there is an integer $d \in I$ such that

$$I = \{x \mid d \text{ divides } x\}.$$

5. Show that, if the three integers a, b, c are not all 0, then they have a unique greatest common divisor. Show that, if at least one of a, b is not 0, then this greatest common divisor is $((a, b), c)$.

9   Prime and relatively prime integers

DEFINITIONS. Two integers a, b are *relatively prime* if at least one of them is not 0 and $(a, b) = 1$. An integer a is *prime* if its only divisors are ± 1 and $\pm a$.

We require that at least one of a, b be non-0 in the definition of 'relatively prime' in order that (a, b) shall exist. If a is prime and b is an integer, then either $(a, b) = 1$ or $(a, b) = |a|$, so either a, b are relatively prime or $a \mid b$. Note that 0 is not prime and that 1, 2, 3 are prime. (In some books, 1, 2 are not considered to be prime integers.)

THEOREM 16. *Two integers a, b are relatively prime if and only if 1 is a linear combination of them.*

Proof. If a, b are relatively prime, then 1 is a linear combination of them, by Theorem 15(i). If 1 is a linear combination of a and b, then every common divisor of a and b divides 1, so the only common divisors of a and b are ± 1. $\square$

THEOREM 17. (i) *If a, b are relatively prime integers and c is an integer such that $a \mid bc$, then $a \mid c$.*

(ii) *If a is a prime integer and a_1, a_2, $a_3, \ldots, a_n$ are integers such that $a \mid \prod_{i=1}^{n} a_i$, then $a \mid a_i$ for some i.*

Proof. (i) By Theorem 16, there are integers s, t such that $1 = sa + tb$. Thus $c = csa + ctb$. Since a divides both csa and ctb, it divides their sum c.

(ii) First we show that (ii) holds if $n = 2$. If $a \mid a_1 a_2$ and a does not divide a_1, then, since a is prime, a and a_1 are relatively prime. Thus, by (i), $a \mid a_2$.

The general case is proved by induction on n. Obviously, (ii) holds if $n = 1$. Suppose it holds if $n = m$, and let a_1, a_2, $a_3, \ldots, a_{m+1}$ be integers such that $a \mid \prod_{i=1}^{m+1} a_i$. Since (ii) holds if $n = m$, a must divide one of $a_1 a_2, a_3, a_4, \ldots, a_{m+1}$. If $a \mid a_1 a_2$ then, by the case $n = 2$, $a \mid a_1$ or $a \mid a_2$. Thus (ii) holds if $n = m + 1$, and this, by the principle of induction, proves (ii). $\square$

THEOREM 18 (*The Unique Factorization Theorem*). *If a is an integer greater than 1, then there is a unique finite sequence of prime integers p_1, p_2, $p_3, \ldots, p_n$, such that $a = \prod_{i=1}^{n} p_i$ and $1 < p_1 \leqslant p_2 \leqslant \ldots \leqslant p_n$.*

Proof. First we show that every integer a which is greater than 1 is a product of prime integers p_1, p_2, $p_3, \ldots, p_n$, such that $1 < p_1 \leqslant p_2 \leqslant p_3 \leqslant \ldots \leqslant p_n$, and we then show that this finite sequence is uniquely determined by a.

Suppose that some integers greater than 1 are not products of such finite sequences. Let a be the least of these integers. Clearly, a cannot be prime, so it has a divisor b which is not ± 1 or $\pm a$. We can suppose that $1 < b < a$ by replacing b by $-b$ if necessary. Thus b is a product of prime integers greater than 1, so there are prime integers greater than 1 which divide a. Let p be the least of these prime integers, and let c be that integer such that $a = pc$. Since $1 < c < a$, there is a finite sequence of prime integers p_1, p_2, $p_3, \ldots, p_n$ whose product is c and such that $1 < p_1 \leqslant p_2 \leqslant p_3 \leqslant \ldots \leqslant p_n$. Obviously, a is the product of $p, p_1, p_2, \ldots, p_n$, and $1 < p \leqslant p_1 \leqslant p_2 \leqslant \ldots \leqslant p_n$; which contradicts the definition of a. Thus every integer greater than 1 can be expressed in the required way.

If some integers greater than 1 can be expressed in two ways, then there is a least such integer a. Let p_1, p_2, $p_3, \ldots, p_n$ and q_1, q_2, $q_3, \ldots, q_m$ be two finite sequences of prime integers whose products are a and which are such that $1 < p_1 \leqslant p_2 \leqslant p_3 \leqslant \ldots \leqslant p_n$ and $1 < q_1 \leqslant q_2 \leqslant q_3 \leqslant \ldots \leqslant q_m$. If $n = 1$ or $m = 1$ then a is prime and hence expressible in only one way, so $n > 1$ and $m > 1$. Also, we can assume that p_1 is the smallest prime integer greater than 1 which divides a. Since $p_1 \mid \prod_{i=1}^{m} q_i$, there is an integer i such that $p_1 \mid q_i$, by theorem 17(ii). Since $p_1 > 1$ and q_i is a positive prime integer, $p_1 = q_i$; and thus, because p_1 is the smallest prime integer dividing a, $p_1 = q_1$.

Therefore $\prod_{i=2}^{n} p_i = \prod_{i=2}^{m} q_i$, these integers existing because $n > 1$ and $m > 1$.

Because $\prod_{i=2}^{n} p_i$ is less than a its factorization is unique, so $n = m$ and $p_i = q_i$ for $i = 2, 3, \ldots, n$. Thus the factorization of a is unique, which contradicts our assumption and proves the theorem. $\square$

The last part of the above proof, showing the uniqueness of factorization, can easily be replaced by an induction proof, but it is not so easy to prove the first part of the theorem by induction on a. It is complicated by the fact that the possibility of factorizing a does not depend on the factorizing of $a - 1$ but on the factorizing of some divisor of a, which might not be $a - 1$.

EXERCISES

1. Show that, if a, b are integers, not both 0, and c, d are the integers such that $a = c \cdot (a, b)$ and $b = d \cdot (a, b)$, then c, d are relatively prime.

2. Show that, if a, b are relatively prime integers, then $(a + b, a - b)$ is 1 or 2.

3. Show that, if a is relatively prime to each of a_1, a_2, a_3, ..., a_n, then it is relatively prime to their product.

4. Show that, if p_1, p_2, p_3, ..., p_n are prime integers, then $\prod_{i=1}^{n} p_i + 1$ is divisible by a prime integer not in the set $\{p_1, p_2, p_3, ..., p_n\}$. Deduce that the set of all prime integers is infinite. (Note that $\prod_{i=1}^{n} p_i + 1$ need not be prime: for example, $3 + 1$, $(3 \cdot 5) + 1$, and $(2 \cdot 3 \cdot 5 \cdot 7 \cdot 11 \cdot 13) + 1$ are not prime.)

5. Prove the first part of Theorem 18 by induction, by considering the statement 'every integer in $]1, n[$ is a product of prime integers'.

10   Least common multiples

DEFINITION. An integer c is a *multiple* of an integer a if a divides c.

If a and b are non-0 integers then they have a common positive multiple, for example $|ab|$, and so have a unique least common positive multiple, which we denote by $[a, b]$. If a or b is 0, then their only common multiple is 0, and in this case we let $[a, b] = 0$.

THEOREM 19. *If c is a common multiple of the integers a, b, then $[a, b] \mid c$.*

Proof. The result is trivial if $a = 0$ or $b = 0$, so suppose that neither a nor b is 0. Then $[a, b] > 0$, so there are integers q, r such that $c = [a, b]q + r$ and $0 \leqslant r < [a, b]$. Since $a \mid c$ and $a \mid [a, b]$, r is a multiple of a. Similarly, r is a multiple of b, so r is a common multiple of a and b which is less than $[a, b]$. Thus $r = 0$, which proves the theorem. □

THEOREM 20. *If at least one of the integers a, b is not 0, then $(a, b) \cdot [a, b] = |ab|$.*

Proof. The result is trivial if $a = 0$ or $b = 0$, so suppose that neither a nor b is 0. Let s be the integer such that $|a| = s \cdot (a, b)$, and let $c = s|b|$. Then $|ab| = c \cdot (a, b)$ where c is a multiple of b. By symmetry, c is also a multiple of a so, by Theorem 19, there is an integer t such that $c = t \cdot [a, b]$. Thus $|ab| = t \cdot [a, b] \cdot (a, b)$. Clearly $t \geqslant 1$, so that $t \cdot (a, b) \geqslant (a, b)$, and thus if we can show that $t \cdot (a, b)$ is a common divisor of a and b then, by the definition of (a, b), t must be 1, and the theorem follows. Let d be that integer such that $[a, b] = db$. Then $|ab| = t \cdot (a, b) \cdot db$, so that $a = \pm t \cdot (a, b) \cdot d$. Thus $t \cdot (a, b) \mid a$. Similarly, $t \cdot (a, b) \mid b$, so $t = 1$. □

EXERCISES

1. Show that, for all non-0 integers a, b, c:

(i) $[a, a+1] = |a(a+1)|$;

(ii) $[ac, ab] = |a| \cdot [c, b]$;

(iii) $(a, b) = (a + b, [a, b])$.

2. Show that, if a, b, c are non-0 integers, then they have a least common positive multiple, which is $[[a, b], c]$.

11 Congruences and residue classes

DEFINITION. If a, b, n are integers such that n divides $b - a$, then a is *congruent to b modulo n*, and we write $a \equiv b\ (n)$.

For a fixed n, the relation of congruence is an equivalence relation:

(i) $n \mid (a - a)$ for all integers a;

(ii) if $n \mid (b - a)$, then $n \mid (a - b)$;

(iii) if n divides $b - a$ and $c - b$, then it divides their sum, which is $c - a$.

Thus $\mathbf{Z}$ is partitioned into disjoint subsets, two integers being in the same subset if and only if their difference is divisible by n. Such a subset of $\mathbf{Z}$ is called a *residue class* modulo n, and the residue class which contains a is denoted by $[a]$. For example, if $n = 3$, then there are just 3 different residue classes:

$$[0] = \{0, 3, -3, 6, -6, 9, \ldots\},$$
$$[1] = \{1, 4, -2, 7, -5, 10, \ldots\},$$
$$[2] = \{2, 5, -1, 8, -4, 11, \ldots\}.$$

In general, if $n \neq 0$ then there are just $|n|$ different residue classes modulo n: by the division theorem, each integer a is congruent modulo n to one and only one integer from the set $]0, |n| - 1[$.

DEFINITIONS. The *sum* $[a] + [b]$ and the *product* $[a][b]$ of the residue classes $[a], [b]$ modulo n, are the residue classes $[a + b], [ab]$ respectively.

The remarks made after the definitions of the sum and product of two integers also apply here: the sum and product of $[a]$ and $[b]$ are found by choosing particular elements from the sets $[a]$ and $[b]$ and then finding the residue classes which contain their sum and product respectively. Thus it is not clear that $[a] + [b]$ and $[a][b]$ are uniquely determined by $[a]$ and $[b]$, and we will now prove this. Suppose that $[a][b]$, for example, is found by choosing c from $[a]$ and d from $[b]$. Then $n \mid (a - c)$ and $n \mid (b - d)$, so that n divides $b(a - c) + c(b - d) = ab - cd$. Thus $[ab]$ and $[cd]$ have the integer ab in common and therefore $[ab] = [cd]$. Similarly, $[a + b] = [c + d]$, so the sum and product of $[a]$ and $[b]$ are uniquely determined by $[a]$ and $[b]$.

THEOREM 21. *If A, B, C are residue classes modulo n, then*:

(i) $(A + B) + C = A + (B + C)$;

(ii) $(AB)C = A(BC)$;

(iii) $A + B = B + A$;

(iv) $AB = BA$;

(v) $A + [0] = A$;

(vi) $A[1] = A$;

(vii) $A(B + C) = AB + AC$;

(viii) *if* $A = [a]$, *then* $A + [-a] = [0]$.

Proof. These properties follow from the corresponding results for the integers which were stated in Theorem 6. For example, if a, b, c are integers then

$$[a]([b] + [c]) = [a]([b + c])$$
$$= [a(b + c)]$$
$$= [ab + ac]$$
$$= [ab] + [ac]$$
$$= [a][b] + [a][c],$$

which proves (vii). □

It follows from Theorem 21 that if A and B are residue classes modulo n, then there is one and only one residue class C such that $A + C = B$, the proof being identical in form to that of Theorem 6(x). The remaining part of Theorem 6, the cancellation law for multiplication, does not have a counterpart here: if $AB = AC$ and $A \neq [0]$, then B and C need not be the same residue class. For example, suppose that n is not prime, so that there are integers a, b such that $n = ab$, $[a] \neq [0]$, and $[b] \neq [0]$. Then

$$[a][b] = [n] = [0] = [a][0],$$

yet $[a]$ cannot be cancelled from both sides of $[a][b] = [a][0]$. Thus, if there is a cancellation law for the multiplication of residue classes modulo n, then n must be prime. The next theorem states that, if n is prime, then there is a cancellation law, and also indicates how this law must be modified if n is not prime.

To simplify the statements and proofs of the remaining theorems of this chapter we will use the following notation: if a, b are integers, $a \mid b$, and $a \neq 0$, then the integer s such that $b = sa$ will be denoted by b/a. Since $a \neq 0$, the integer b/a is uniquely determined by the ordered pair $\langle a, b \rangle$. In the next chapter a meaning will be given to the symbol b/a even if a does not divide b – that is, the rational numbers will be defined – but for the remainder of this chapter b/a will have a meaning only if $a \mid b$ and $a \neq 0$.

THEOREM 22. (i) *If a, b, c, n are integers, at least one of a, n is not 0, and* $ab \equiv ac\ (n)$, *then* $b \equiv c\ (n/(a, n))$.

(ii) *If A is a residue class modulo n, n is prime, and $A \neq [0]$, then there is a residue class D such that $AD = [1]$.*

(iii) *If A, B, C are residue classes modulo n, n is prime, $A \neq [0]$, and $AB = AC$, then $B = C$.*

Proof. (i) Since at least one of a, n is not 0, (a, n) exists. Let s be the integer such that $a(b - c) = sn$. Then

$$(a/(a, n)) \cdot (b - c) = s \cdot (n/(a, n)).$$

By Theorem 15(i), (a, n) is a linear combination of a and n, and so 1 is a linear combination of $a/(a, n)$ and $n/(a, n)$. Thus, by Theorem 16, $a/(a, n)$ and $n/(a, n)$ are relatively prime; and hence, from the above equation and Theorem 17(i), $n/(a, n) \mid (b - c)$.

(ii) Let $A = [a]$. Since n is prime, either $n \mid a$ or a and n are relatively prime. If $n \mid a$ then $A = [0]$, so a and n are relatively prime. Thus there are integers s, t such that

$$1 = sa + tn.$$

Let $D = [s]$. Then $[1] = [sa] = AD$.

(iii) follows from (i) or (ii). To prove it from (i), simply note that if $A = [a] \neq 0$, then $(a, n) = 1$. To prove (iii) from (ii), multiply both sides of $AB = AC$ by D and use Theorem 21 to obtain $B = C$. □

EXERCISES

1. Write out addition and multiplication tables for the set of residue classes modulo 4 and for the set of residue classes modulo 5.

2. Let n be a prime integer and let A be a residue class modulo n such that $A \neq [0]$. Show that the residue class D such that $AD = [1]$ is unique. Denote D by A^{-1}. Show that $(AB)^{-1} = A^{-1}B^{-1}$, where $B \neq [0]$, and find necessary and sufficient conditions on A in order that $A = A^{-1}$.

3. Let n be a prime integer and let $\{A_1, A_2, A_3, \ldots\}$ be the set of non-[0] residue classes modulo n. Show that $\{A_1 A_1, A_1 A_2, A_1 A_3, \ldots\}$ is also the set of non-[0] residue classes modulo n, and deduce Theorem 22(ii) from Theorem 22(i) and (iii).

4. If n is a prime integer greater than 1, and a is not divisible by n, show that no two of the integers

$$a, 2a, 3a, \ldots, (n-1)a$$

are congruent modulo n. Thus show that $\prod_{i=1}^{n-1} ia$ is congruent modulo n to $\prod_{i=1}^{n-1} i$. Deduce that $a^{n-1} \equiv 1 \ (n)$ (Fermat's theorem).

5. Using Fermat's theorem and Exercise 9, p. 23, show that if n is a prime integer greater than 2, and a, b are integers such that $a^n + b^n \equiv 0 \ (n)$, then $a^n + b^n \equiv 0 \ (n^2)$.

12   The solution of congruences in one unknown

THEOREM 23. *Let a, b, n be integers, at least one of a, n being non-0. If there is an integer x such that $ax \equiv b$ (n), then $(a, n) \mid b$. If $(a, n) \mid b$, then there is an integer x such that $ax \equiv b$ (n), and the set of such x is a residue class modulo $n/(a, n)$.*

Proof. Since at least one of a, n is non-0, (a, n) exists.

Suppose that there is an integer x such that $ax \equiv b$ (n). Then b is a linear combination of a and n. Since (a, n) divides every linear combination of a and n, it must divide b.

Now suppose that $(a, n) \mid b$, and let $e = b/(a, n)$. By Theorem 15(i), there are integers c, d such that $(a, n) = ca + dn$, from which $a(ce) \equiv b$ (n). Thus $ax \equiv b$ (n) has a solution. Let $z = ce$, so that $az \equiv b$ (n). To complete the proof, we must show that $ax \equiv b$ (n) if and only if $x \equiv z$ $(n/(a, n))$. If $ax \equiv b$ (n), then $ax \equiv az$ (n) so that, by Theorem 22(i), $x \equiv z$ $(n/(a, n))$. If x is an integer such that $x \equiv z$ $(n/(a, n))$, let s be the integer such that $x - z = sn/(a, n)$. Then $ax - az = n(sa/(a, n))$, so that $ax \equiv az \equiv b$ (n). □

EXAMPLE. The congruence $15x \equiv 6$ (12) is solvable because $(15, 12) \mid 6$. To solve it, list the integers congruent to 6 modulo 12 until a multiple of 15 is obtained: $6, 18, 30, \ldots$. Thus, $x = 2$ is a solution, and the set of all solutions is the residue class $[2]$ modulo 4.

THEOREM 24. *Let a, b, c, d be integers, at least one of a, b being non-0. If there is an integer x such that $x \equiv c$ (a) and $x \equiv d$ (b), then $d \equiv c$ $((a, b))$. Conversely, if $d \equiv c$ $((a, b))$, then there is an integer x such that $x \equiv c$ (a) and $x \equiv d$ (b). If $d \equiv c$ $((a, b))$, then the set of such x is a residue class modulo $[a, b]$.*

Proof. Since at least one of a, b is non-0, (a, b) exists. Suppose that there is an integer x satisfying both congruences. Then $x \equiv c$ $((a, b))$ and $x \equiv d$ $((a, b))$, so that $d \equiv c$ $((a, b))$.

Now suppose that $d \equiv c$ $((a, b))$ and let s, t be integers such that $d - c = sa + tb$. The integer

$$z = d - tb = sa + c$$

clearly satisfies both congruences.

To complete the proof, we must show that x satisfies both congruences if and only if $x \equiv z$ $([a, b])$. Suppose that x satisfies both congruences. Then $z \equiv x$ (a) and $z \equiv x$ (b), so that $z - x$ is a common multiple of a and b. By Theorem 19, $x \equiv z$ $([a, b])$. Now suppose that x is an integer which is congruent to z modulo $[a, b]$. Since $a \mid [a, b]$ and $[a, b] \mid (x - z)$, therefore $a \mid (x - z)$. Thus $x \equiv z \equiv c$ (a). Similarly $x \equiv d$ (b). □

EXAMPLE. The congruences $x \equiv 5\ (6)$ and $x \equiv 9\ (10)$ have a common solution because $5 \equiv 9\ (2)$. The solutions to the first congruence are those integers which are of the form $5 + 6t$, where t is any integer, so to solve the second congruence as well we must find an integer t such that $5 + 6t \equiv 9\ (10)$, that is, we must solve $6t \equiv 4\ (10)$. Listing the integers congruent to 4 modulo 10: 4, 14, 24,..., we find that $t = 4$ is a solution. Thus $5 + (6 \cdot 4) = 29$ is a common solution to the two original congruences, and the set of all common solutions is the residue class [29] modulo 30.

The next theorem was known to the Chinese in the fourth century and is sometimes called the *Chinese Remainder Theorem*. The generalization of Theorem 24 which is set as Exercise 4 was also known to the Chinese at that time, their proof apparently depending on Theorem 25.[1]

THEOREM 25. *If $a_1, a_2, a_3,\ldots, a_n$ are non-0 integers such that $(a_i, a_j) = 1$ if $i \neq j$, and $b_1, b_2, b_3,\ldots, b_n$ are integers, then the set of integers x such that*

$$x \equiv b_i\ (a_i)\ for\ i = 1, 2, 3,\ldots, n,$$

is a residue class modulo $\prod_{i=1}^{n} a_i$.

Proof. We proceed by induction on n. The result is obvious if $n = 1$ and follows easily from Theorem 24 if $n = 2$. Suppose that the set of integers x such that $x \equiv b_i\ (a_i)$ for $i = 1, 2, 3,\ldots, n-1$ is a residue class modulo $\prod_{i=1}^{n-1} a_i$. Let c be a member of this residue class. Then $x \equiv b_i\ (a_i)$ for $i = 1, 2, 3,\ldots, n$ if and only if $x \equiv c \left(\prod_{i=1}^{n-1} a_i \right)$ and $x \equiv b_n\ (a_n)$. Since a_n is relatively prime to each of $a_1, a_2, a_3,\ldots, a_{n-1}$, it is relatively prime to their product, and so, by Theorem 24, the set of x such that $x \equiv b_i\ (a_i)$ for $i = 1, 2, 3,\ldots, n$ is a residue class modulo $\left[a_n, \prod_{i=1}^{n-1} a_i \right]$. By Theorem 20, $\left[a_n, \prod_{i=1}^{n-1} a_i \right] = \left| \prod_{i=1}^{n} a_i \right|$, which, by the principle of induction, completes the proof. □

Theorem 25 can also be stated in terms of residue classes: *If $a_1, a_2, a_3,\ldots, a_n$ are relatively prime in pairs, and $A_1, A_2, A_3,\ldots, A_n$ are residue classes modulo $a_1, a_2, a_3,\ldots, a_n$ respectively, then the intersection of $A_1, A_2, A_3,\ldots, A_n$ is a residue class modulo $\prod_{i=1}^{n} a_i$.*

The remarks following the proof of Theorem 11 also apply to the proof

[1] For a full discussion, see K. Mahler, On the Chinese remainder theorem, *Math. Nachrichten*, **18** (1958), pp. 120–122.

of Theorem 25: the particular case $n = 2$, which is the first non-trivial case, required a separate proof since it was used in the proof of Theorem 25. The proof of Theorem 25 is also interesting for another reason. If we had only attempted to show that the n congruences have a common solution, not that the set of solutions is a residue class, then it would have been far more difficult to reduce the n congruences to two and thus prove the theorem. That is, it would have been more difficult to prove a weaker result. This situation often arises in induction proofs – the required result must be weak enough to be provable but strong enough to be self-propagating.

THEOREM 26. *If a, b, c, d, m, n are integers such that $(m, n) = 1$, $(a, m) \mid b$, and $(c, n) \mid d$, then the set of integers x such that $ax \equiv b \ (m)$ and $cx \equiv d \ (n)$ is a residue class modulo $mn/((a, m) \cdot (c, n))$.*

Proof. By Theorems 23 and 24, there are integers s, t, u, v such that $as \equiv b \ (m)$, $ct \equiv d \ (n)$, $u \equiv 1 (m)$, $u \equiv 0 \ (n)$, $v \equiv 0 \ (m)$, and $v \equiv 1 (n)$. From these relations it is easy to show that

$$z = su + tv$$

is a solution to both of the given congruences. To complete the proof we must show that x is a solution to both of these congruences if and only if x is congruent to z modulo $mn/((a, m) \cdot (c, n))$. Suppose that x is a solution to both congruences. Then $a(x - z) \equiv 0 \ (m)$ and $c(x - z) \equiv 0 \ (n)$. By Theorem 22(i), $x - z$ is divisible by both $m/(a, m)$ and $n/(c, n)$. The integers $m/(a, m)$, $n/(c, n)$ are relatively prime because m and n are relatively prime, and so $x - z$ is divisible by their product (see Exercise 2(iii), p. 26).

Now suppose that x is congruent to z modulo $mn/((a, m) \cdot (c, n))$. Then $ax - az$ is a multiple of $amn/((a, m) \cdot (c, n))$, which is itself a multiple of m, so that $ax \equiv az \equiv b \ (m)$. Similarly, $cx \equiv d \ (n)$. □

EXERCISES

1. Find all the solutions to each of the following congruences: $8x \equiv 4 \ (12)$; $2x \equiv 1 \ (5)$; $6x \equiv 9 \ (3)$.

2. Find all the solutions to each of the following pairs of congruences:
(i) $8x \equiv 4 \ (12)$, $2x \equiv 1 \ (5)$;
(ii) $2x \equiv 1 \ (5)$, $6x \equiv 9 \ (3)$;
(iii) $8x \equiv 4 \ (12)$; $6x \equiv 9 \ (3)$;
(iv) $9x \equiv 5 \ (4)$; $7x \equiv 1 \ (9)$.

3. Find all the solutions common to the three congruences $x \equiv 1 (2)$, $x \equiv 2 \ (3)$, $x \equiv 3 \ (5)$.

4. Let a_1, a_2, $a_3, \ldots, a_n$ be non-0 integers and let b_1, b_2, $b_3, \ldots, b_n$ be integers. Show that the n congruences $x \equiv b_i \ (a_i)$ for $i = 1, 2, 3, \ldots, n$, have a common

solution if and only if $b_i \equiv b_j \, ((a_i, a_j))$ for all $i, j = 1, 2, 3, \ldots, n$. Show that if there is a common solution, then the set of common solutions is a residue class modulo the least common multiple of $a_1, a_2, a_3, \ldots, a_n$.

5. Prove that if $(a, b) = (c, d) = 1$, then $ax \equiv e \,(b)$ and $cx \equiv f \,(d)$ have a common solution if and only if $ec \equiv fa \,((b, d))$.

6. Prove that $ax \equiv b \,(m)$ has a solution which is relatively prime to m if and only if $(a, m) = (b, m)$.

CHAPTER 2

THE RATIONAL, REAL, AND COMPLEX NUMBERS

1   The rational numbers

If a, b are integers, then the equation $bx = a$ does not necessarily have an integral solution x. That is, b does not necessarily divide a. Now we will embed the set of integers in a set $\mathbf{Q}$, the set of rational numbers, in which $bx = a$ can always be solved uniquely if $b \neq 0$. We proceed in much the same way as we did in §4 of Chapter 1, where we embedded $\mathbf{Z}^+$ in $\mathbf{Z}$, and remarks similar to those made there also apply here.

Suppose, for the moment, that we have obtained the required extension $\mathbf{Q}$. Then the solution to $bx = a$ is uniquely determined by $\langle a, b \rangle$, and it is easily verified that if the usual laws of arithmetic hold, then $bx = a$ and $ex = d$ have a common solution if and only if $ae = bd$, where a, b, d, $e \in \mathbf{Z}$, $b \neq 0$, and $e \neq 0$. Thus each element of $\mathbf{Q}$ is uniquely associated with a set of ordered pairs of integers, two ordered pairs $\langle a, b \rangle$, $\langle d, e \rangle$ being in the same set if and only if $ae = bd$, $b \neq 0$, and $e \neq 0$.

Thus, to construct $\mathbf{Q}$, we consider the relation α defined on the set $A = \{\langle a, b \rangle \mid a, b \in \mathbf{Z} \text{ and } b \neq 0\}$ by '$\langle a, b \rangle \, \alpha \, \langle d, e \rangle$ if and only if $ae = bd$'. This relation is an equivalence relation on A. The first two properties of an equivalence relation follow immediately from the commutativity of multiplication of the integers. To show that the third property holds, suppose that $\langle a, b \rangle \, \alpha \, \langle d, e \rangle$ and $\langle d, e \rangle \, \alpha \, \langle f, g \rangle$. Then $ae = bd$ and $dg = ef$, so that $aeg = bdg = bef$. Since $e \neq 0$, $ag = bf$, and thus $\langle a, b \rangle \, \alpha \, \langle f, g \rangle$.

DEFINITIONS. A *rational number* is an equivalence class determined by the relation α on the set $\{\langle a, b \rangle \mid a, b \in \mathbf{Z} \text{ and } b \neq 0\}$ that is defined by '$\langle a, b \rangle \, \alpha \, \langle d, e \rangle$ if and only if $ae = bd$'.

The rational number containing $\langle a, b \rangle$ is denoted by a/b, and the set of rational numbers is denoted by $\mathbf{Q}$. The *sum* $a/b + d/e$ of the rational numbers a/b, d/e is the rational number $(ae + bd)/be$, and their *product* $(a/b)(d/e)$ is ad/be. The rational number $-a/b$ is denoted by $-(a/b)$, and the sum $n + (-m)$ of the rational numbers n, $-m$ is denoted by $n - m$.

The sum and product of any two rational numbers a/b, d/e exist, since $be \neq 0$. To show that $a/b + d/e$ is uniquely determined by the ordered pair

$\langle a/b, d/e \rangle$, suppose that $a'/b' = a/b$ and $d'/e' = d/e$. Then $a'b = b'a$ and $d'e = e'd$, from which it easily follows that $(ae + bd)b'e' = be(a'e' + b'd')$. Thus $\langle ae + bd, be \rangle \propto \langle a'e' + b'd', b'e' \rangle$, so that $a/b + d/e$ and $a'/b' + d'/e'$ have a common element and hence are equal. Similarly, the product of two rational numbers n, m does not depend on the particular elements chosen from the sets n, m.

THEOREM 1. *If a, b, c are rational numbers, then*:
(i) $(a + b) + c = a + (b + c)$;
(ii) $(ab)c = a(bc)$;
(iii) $a + b = b + a$;
(iv) $ab = ba$;
(v) $a + (0/1) = a$;
(vi) $a(1/1) = a$;
(vii) $a(b + c) = ab + ac$;
(viii) $a - a = 0/1$;
(ix) *if $ab = ac$ and $a \neq 0/1$, then $b = c$*;
(x) *there is one and only one rational number x such that $a + x = b$; it is $b - a$*;
(xi) *if $b \neq 0/1$, then there is one and only one rational number x such that $bx = a$*.

Proof. The first ten results follow from the definitions and Theorem 6 of Chapter 1. For example, to prove (ix), let a, b, c be the rational numbers d/e, f/g, h/i respectively. Then $dfei = egdh$ and, since $a \neq 0/1$, $d \neq 0$. Also, $e \neq 0$ by the definition of rational number. Thus, by the results of Theorem 6, we have $fi = gh$, so that $b = c$.

To prove (xi), let b, a be the rational numbers d/e, f/g respectively, and let $x = ef/dg$. Since $dg \neq 0$, x is a rational number, and it is easy to verify that $bx = a$. The uniqueness of x follows immediately from (ix). $\square$

The associative and commutative properties stated as (i), (ii), (iii), (iv) in the above theorem can be generalized to any finite number of terms; the results and their proofs are obtained by simply substituting 'rational number' for 'integer' in the relevant parts of §7, Chapter 1. We will use these results without further comment.

Now we will embed $\mathbf{Z}$ in $\mathbf{Q}$. By the remarks in §4 of Chapter 1, we must find an injection f from $\mathbf{Z}$ to $\mathbf{Q}$ such that $f(a + b) = f(a) + f(b)$ and $f(ab) = f(a)f(b)$ for all a, $b \in \mathbf{Z}$. Our choice of injection is suggested by the observation that each integer a is the solution to the equation $1x = a$; let f be the function from $\mathbf{Z}$ to $\mathbf{Q}$ defined by the equation

$$f(a) = a/1$$

for all $a \in \mathbf{Z}$. It is easy to verify that f is an injection which satisfies the required conditions. Thus $\mathbf{Z}$ can be embedded in $\mathbf{Q}$ by replacing $a/1$ by a, for each $a \in \mathbf{Z}$, but regarding a as $a/1$ for the purpose of calculation. As we saw in §4, this cannot lead to any ambiguity. Thus we now regard a and $a/1$ as identical, and we have therefore embedded $\mathbf{Z}$ in a set $\mathbf{Q}$ in which $bx = a$ has a unique solution if $b \neq 0$.

DEFINITIONS. If a, b are rational numbers, and there is a positive integer c such that $c(a - b)$ is a positive integer, then *a is greater than b*, and this is denoted by $a > b$. By *b is less than a*, denoted by $b < a$, we mean that a is greater than b. If $a > b$ or $a = b$, then this is denoted by $a \geqslant b$ or by $b \leqslant a$.

Since every integer is a rational number, the relation $>$ between integers has now been defined in two ways, once in Chapter 1, regarding the integers only as integers, and now regarding them as rational numbers. To show that these definitions are compatible, we note that:
(i) if a, b are integers and $a > b$ (as integers), then $1(a - b)$ is a positive integer, so that $a > b$ (as rational numbers);
(ii) if a, b are integers and $a \leqslant b$ (as integers), then, for all positive integers c, $c(a - b)$ is not a positive integer. Therefore, if $a > b$ (as rational numbers), then $a > b$ (as integers).

THEOREM 2. *If a, b are rational numbers, then*:
(i) *either $a > b$, $a < b$, or $a = b$*;
(ii) *if $a \geqslant b$ and $a \leqslant b$, then $a = b$*;
(iii) *if $a \neq 0$, then there is an integer n such that $b < na$.*

Proof. Let $a = c/d$ and $b = e/f$, where c, d, e, f are integers, $d > 0$, and $f > 0$. (We can assume that $d > 0$ and $f > 0$, because if, for example, $d < 0$, then $-d > 0$ and $a = -c/-d$.) The integer df is positive, and $df(a - b) = fc - de$ is an integer which (by Theorem 7, p. 13) is positive, negative, or 0. If $df(a - b) > 0$, then $a > b$; if $df(a - b) < 0$, then $df(b - a) > 0$, and therefore $b > a$; and if $df(a - b) = 0$, then $fc = de$, so that $a = b$. This proves (i).

If $a \leqslant b$, $a \geqslant b$, and $a \neq b$, then there are positive integers n, m such that $n(b - a)$ and $m(a - b)$ are positive integers. Since the sum and product of positive integers are positive,

$$mn(b - a) + nm(a - b) = 0$$

is a positive integer. This is not true, so that if $a \leqslant b$ and $a \geqslant b$ then $a = b$.

To prove the third part, we must find an integer n such that $ncf > ed$, where $c \neq 0$. The existence of such an integer follows immediately from the inequalities

$$|ed+1||cf| \geq |ed+1| > ed. \quad \square$$

EXERCISES

1. Prove that, for all rational numbers a, b, (i) $-(-a)=a$; (ii) $0a=0$; (iii) $a(-b)=-(ab)$; (iv) $(-a)(-b)=ab$.

2. Let a be a non-0 rational number. Show that there are unique integers c, d such that $a=c/d$, $d>0$, and c and d are relatively prime. Show that, if $a=e/f$, then there is an integer n such that $e=nc$ and $f=nd$.

3. Let g be an injection from $\mathbf{Z}$ to $\mathbf{Q}$ such that $g(a+b)=g(a)+g(b)$ and $g(ab)=g(a)g(b)$ for all a, $b \in \mathbf{Z}$. Show that $g(a)=a/1$ for all $a \in \mathbf{Z}$.

4. Let a, b be rational numbers, $a \neq 0$. By Theorem 1(xi), there is a unique rational number x such that $ax=b$; denote it by b/a. If a, b are integers, then the rational number b/a has been defined in two ways. Show that these definitions are compatible. Let a, b, c, d be rational numbers, $a \neq 0$ and $c \neq 0$. Show that

$$b/a + d/c = (bc+da)/ac$$

and
$$(b/a)(d/c) = bd/ac.$$

5. Show that if a, b, c are rational numbers such that $a < b$, then:
(i) $a+c < b+c$;
(ii) if $0 < c$, then $ac < bc$; if $0 > c$, then $ac > bc$;
(iii) if $b > 0$ and $c > 0$, and $b^2 < c^2$, then $b < c$;
(iv) if $a < a/2$, then $a < 0$;
(v) if $b < c$, then $a < c$;
(vi) $a < (a+b)/2 < b$;
(vii) $0 \leq c^2$, and $0 = c^2$ if and only if $c = 0$.

6. Let a be a rational number such that $a \leq b$ for every rational number $b > 0$. Show that $a \leq 0$.

7. Define the *absolute value* $|a|$ of a rational number a to be a if $a \geq 0$ and $-a$ if $a < 0$. Show that, for every integer, this definition agrees with that given in Exercise 5, p. 15, and that, for all rational numbers a, b, c:
(i) $|a+b| \leq |a| + |b|$;
(ii) $|a-b| \leq |a-c| + |c-b|$;
(iii) $|ab| = |a||b|$.

2 The real numbers

We now extend the set of rational numbers to the set of real numbers by considering the convergence of sequences of rational numbers. The term 'sequence' was defined on p. 18.

DEFINITION. A *Cauchy sequence of rational numbers* is an infinite sequence $(a_i)_i$ of rational numbers with the property: with each rational number $\epsilon > 0$ there can be associated an integer N such that $|a_n - a_m| < \epsilon$ whenever $n \geqslant N$ and $m \geqslant N$. A rational number a is the *limit* of an infinite sequence $(a_i)_i$ of rational numbers if it has the property: with each rational number $\epsilon > 0$ there can be associated an integer N such that $|a - a_n| < \epsilon$ whenever $n \geqslant N$.

EXAMPLES. (i) The sequence $(1/i)_i$ has the limit 0. Let $\epsilon > 0$ be a rational number. Then

$$|0 - 1/n| = 1/n < \epsilon$$

if $n > 1/\epsilon$. Let N be an integer greater than $1/\epsilon$ (there is such an integer by the last part of Theorem 2). If $n \geqslant N$, then $|0 - 1/n| < \epsilon$.

(ii) The sequence $(i)_i$ is not a Cauchy sequence. Let $\epsilon = 1/2$. Then $|n - m| < \epsilon$ only if $n = m$. Thus for this ϵ there is no corresponding integer N.

We now consider a particularly important example – we will construct a Cauchy sequence of rational numbers which does not have a rational number for a limit. Let n be a positive integer. The set $\{m \mid m$ is a positive integer and $m^2 < 2n^2\}$ is not empty – it obviously contains 1 – and it is bounded above, for example by $2n$. Thus it contains a greatest member, which we denote by $f(n)$.

We now show that the sequence $(f(i)/i)_i$ is a Cauchy sequence which does not have a rational number for a limit. By the definition of $f(n)$,

$$(f(n)/n)^2 < 2 \leqslant ((f(n) + 1)/n)^2,$$

so that

$$(f(n)/n)^2 < ((f(m) + 1)/m)^2$$

for all positive integers n, m. Therefore, by Exercise 5(iii), p. 40,

$$f(n)/n < (f(m) + 1)/m$$

for all n, m. Thus $(f(n)/n - f(m)/m) < 1/m$, so that $|f(n)/n - f(m)/m|$ is less than the larger of $1/n$, $1/m$. Therefore,

$$|f(n)/n - f(m)/m| < 1/n + 1/m$$

for all positive integers n, m.

Now we show that $(f(i)/i)_i$ is a Cauchy sequence. Let $\epsilon > 0$ be a rational number. Then

$$|f(n)/n - f(m)/m| < 1/n + 1/m < \epsilon,$$

provided that $1/n < \epsilon/2$ and $1/m < \epsilon/2$. Let N be an integer greater than $2/\epsilon$. If $n \geqslant N$ and $m \geqslant N$, then $|f(n)/n - f(m)/m| < \epsilon$, so that $(f(i)/i)_i$ is a Cauchy sequence.

4

We show finally that $(f(i)/i)_i$ does not have a rational number for a limit by first showing that if a is the limit of $(f(i)/i)_i$ then $a^2 = 2$, and then showing that there is no rational number satisfying this equation.

Let a be a rational number and let n be a positive integer. By Exercise 7, p. 40,

$$|a^2 - 2| \leqslant |a^2 - (f(n)/n)^2| + |(f(n)/n)^2 - 2|$$
$$\leqslant |a - f(n)/n||a + f(n)/n| + |(f(n)/n)^2 - 2|.$$

Since $(f(n)/n)^2 < 2 < 4$ we have $|f(n)/n| < 2$, so that $|a + f(n)/n| < |a| + 2$. By the inequalities defining $f(n)$,

$$0 < 2 - (f(n)/n)^2 \leqslant 1/n^2 + 2f(n)/n^2 < 1/n^2 + 4/n,$$

so that $|(f(n)/n)^2 - 2| < 5/n$. Therefore,

$$|a^2 - 2| < |a - f(n)/2|(|a| + 2) + 5/n$$

for all rational numbers a and all positive integers n. Now suppose that a is the limit of $(f(i)/i)_i$. Let $\epsilon > 0$ be a rational number and let N be an integer such that $|a - f(n)/n| < \epsilon$ if $n \geqslant N$. If $n \geqslant N$, then

$$|a^2 - 2| < \epsilon(|a| + 2) + 5/n.$$

Let $b > 0$ be a rational number and suppose that we have chosen $\epsilon = b/2(|a| + 2)$. Then

$$|a^2 - 2| < b/2 + 5/n$$

for all $n \geqslant N$, so if we now chose $n \geqslant N$ and $n \geqslant 10/b$, then

$$|a^2 - 2| < b.$$

Thus $|a^2 - 2|$ is a rational number which is less than every rational number $b > 0$. By Exercise 6, p. 40, $|a^2 - 2| \leqslant 0$, so that $a^2 = 2$. [The solution to Exercise 6 is as follows: if $a > 0$ then $a \leqslant a/2$, because $a/2 > 0$. This is impossible, by 5(iv), so $a \leqslant 0$].

Now we show that there is no rational number a such that $a^2 = 2$. Suppose that there is such a rational number $a = b/c$, where b, c are relatively prime integers, $c > 0$ (see Exercise 2, p. 40). Let n, m be integers such that $1 = bn + cm$. Then

$$b = b^2 n + cbm = c(2cn + bm),$$

so that $c \mid b$, and therefore $c = 1$. That is, a is an integer. If $|a| \geqslant 2$ then $a^2 \geqslant 4$, so that $|a| < 2$. But if $|a| < 2$ then $|a| = 0$ or 1, and neither 0^2 nor 1^2 is 2. Thus there is no rational number a such that $a^2 = 2$.

Our objective in defining the real numbers is to obtain a set $\mathbf{R}$ which contains $\mathbf{Q}$, has all the algebraic properties of $\mathbf{Q}$ as expressed in Theorem 1,

p. 38, and contains a unique limit for each Cauchy sequence of rational numbers.

Suppose, for the moment, that we have obtained such an extension **R**. Then, each Cauchy sequence of rational numbers determines a unique element of **R**, the limit of the sequence. Suppose that two such sequences $(a_i)_i$, $(b_i)_i$, have the same limit a. Let $\epsilon > 0$ be a rational number and let N, M be integers such that, if $n \geqslant N$ then $|a - a_n| < \epsilon/2$, and if $n \geqslant M$ then $|a - b_n| < \epsilon/2$. Let R be the larger of N, M. If $n \geqslant R$, then

$$|a_n - b_n| \leqslant |a_n - a| + |a - b_n| < \epsilon/2 + \epsilon/2 = \epsilon.$$

Thus, if $(a_i)_i$ and $(b_i)_i$ have the same limit, then they are related in the following way: with each rational number $\epsilon > 0$ there can be associated an integer N such that $|a_n - b_n| < \epsilon$ if $n \geqslant N$. Now suppose that $(a_i)_i$, $(b_i)_i$ are Cauchy sequences of rational numbers which are related as above, and suppose that $(a_i)_i$ has the limit a. Let $\epsilon > 0$ be a rational number and let R, N be integers such that: if $n \geqslant R$ then $|a_n - b_n| < \epsilon/2$; if $n \geqslant N$ then $|a - a_n| < \epsilon/2$. Let M be the larger of R, N. If $n \geqslant M$, then

$$|a - b_n| \leqslant |a - a_n| + |a_n - b_n| < \epsilon/2 + \epsilon/2 = \epsilon.$$

Thus, a is the limit of $(b_i)_i$, so that two Cauchy sequences of rational numbers have the same limit if and only if they are related as above.

Thus, in order to construct **R**, we consider the relation α defined on the set of all Cauchy sequences of rational numbers by '$(a_i)_i \alpha (b_i)_i$ if and only if, with each rational number $\epsilon > 0$, there can be associated an integer N such that $|a_n - b_n| < \epsilon$ if $n \geqslant N$'. This relation is an equivalence relation: the first two properties of an equivalence relation obviously hold and the third follows easily from the inequality

$$|a_n - c_n| \leqslant |a_n - b_n| + |b_n - c_n|,$$

which holds for all rational numbers a_n, b_n, c_n.

DEFINITIONS. A *real number* is an equivalence class determined by the relation α on the set of all Cauchy sequences of rational numbers that is defined by '$(a_i)_i \alpha (b_i)_i$ if and only if with each rational number $\epsilon > 0$ there can be associated an integer N such that $|a_n - b_n| < \epsilon$ whenever $n > N$'.

The real number containing $(a_i)_i$ is denoted by $[(a_i)_i]$, and the set of real numbers is denoted by **R**. The *sum* $[(a_i)_i] + [(b_i)_i]$ of the real numbers $[(a_i)_i]$, $[(b_i)_i]$ is the real number $[(a_i + b_i)_i]$ and their *product* $[(a_i)_i] [(b_i)_i]$ is $[(a_i b_i)_i]$. The real number $[(-a_i)_i]$ is denoted by $-[(a_i)_i]$, and the sum $n + (-m)$ of the real numbers n, $-m$ is denoted by $n - m$.

These definitions must satisfy the usual requirements:

(i) We must show that the sum and product of two real numbers are real numbers. That is, we must show that if $(a_i)_i$ and $(b_i)_i$ are Cauchy sequences of rational numbers, then $(a_i + b_i)_i$ and $(a_ib_i)_i$ are also Cauchy sequences of rational numbers. Both $(a_i + b_i)_i$ and $(a_ib_i)_i$ are sequences of rational numbers, because the sum and product of any two rational numbers are rational numbers. The Cauchy property of $(a_i + b_i)_i$ follows immediately from the inequality

$$|(a_n + b_n) - (a_m + b_m)| \leqslant |a_n - a_m| + |b_n - b_m|.$$

It is considerably more difficult to show that $(a_ib_i)_i$ is a Cauchy sequence. Since $(a_i)_i$ is a Cauchy sequence, there is an integer N such that $|a_n - a_m| < 1$ if $n \geqslant N$ and $m \geqslant N$. Thus, if $n \geqslant N$, then $|a_n| < 1 + |a_N|$. Similarly, there is an integer M such that, if $n \geqslant M$, then $|b_n| < 1 + |b_M|$. Let $\delta > 0$ be a rational number. Since $(a_i)_i$ and $(b_i)_i$ are Cauchy sequences, there is an integer R, which can be chosen to be greater than N and M, such that $|a_n - a_m| < \delta$ and $|b_n - b_m| < \delta$ if $n \geqslant R$ and $m \geqslant R$. Suppose that $n \geqslant R$ and $m \geqslant R$. Then

$$|(a_nb_n) - (a_mb_m)| \leqslant |a_n||b_n - b_m| + |b_m||a_n - a_m|$$
$$< (2 + (|a_N| + |b_M|))\delta.$$

If $\epsilon > 0$ is any given rational number, we can choose as δ the number $\epsilon/(2 + (|a_N| + |b_M|))$. If $n \geqslant R$ and $m \geqslant R$, then

$$|(a_nb_n) - (a_mb_m)| < \epsilon,$$

so that $(a_ib_i)_i$ is a Cauchy sequence of rational numbers.

(ii) We must show that the sum and product of the real numbers $[(a_i)_i]$ and $[(b_i)_i]$ are uniquely determined by the ordered pair $\langle [(a_i)_i], [(b_i)_i] \rangle$. Suppose that $(a_i)_i \propto (c_i)_i$ and $(b_i)_i \propto (d_i)_i$. It follows immediately from

$$|(a_n + b_n) - (c_n + d_n)| \leqslant |a_n - c_n| + |b_n - d_n|$$

that $(a_i + b_i)_i \propto (c_i + d_i)_i$, so that the sum of $[(a_i)_i]$ and $[(b_i)_i]$ is uniquely determined by $\langle [(a_i)_i], [(b_i)_i] \rangle$. The proof that $[(a_i)_i] [(b_i)_i]$ is uniquely determined by $\langle [(a_i)_i], [(b_i)_i] \rangle$ is left to the reader.

THEOREM 3. *If a, b, c are real numbers, then*:

(i) $(a + b) + c = a + (b + c)$;

(ii) $(ab)c = a(bc)$;

(iii) $a + b = b + a$;

(iv) $ab = ba$;

(v) $a + [(0)_i] = a$;

(vi) $a[(1)_i] = a$;

(vii) $a(b + c) = ab + ac$;

(viii) $a - a = [(0)_i]$;

(ix) *if* $ab = ac$ *and* $a \neq [(0)_i]$, *then* $b = c$;

(x) *there is one and only one real number* x *such that* $a + x = b$; *it is* $b - a$;

(xi) *if* $a \neq [(0)_i]$, *then there is one and only one real number* x *such that* $ax = b$.

Proof. Results (i)–(viii) and (x) are quite easy to prove and are left to the reader. In order to prove (ix) and (xi), it is sufficient to show that there is a real number d such that $ad = [(1)_i]$. Result (ix) then follows from

$$(b - c) = ad(b - c) = d(ab - ac) = [(0)_i],$$

and (xi) follows from

$$b = (ad)b = a(db)$$

and (ix).

Let $a = [(a_i)_i]$. Since $a \neq [(0)_i]$, the relation $(a_i)_i \propto (0)_i$ does not hold. Therefore there is a rational number $\delta > 0$ with the property: given an integer N, there is an integer n such that $n \geqslant N$ and $|a_n - 0| \geqslant \delta$. Since $(a_i)_i$ is a Cauchy sequence, there is an integer M such that $|a_n - a_m| < \delta/2$ if $n \geqslant M$ and $m \geqslant M$. Suppose that $m \geqslant M$. There is an integer $n \geqslant M$ such that $|a_n| \geqslant \delta$. Thus

$$|a_m| \geqslant |a_n| - |a_m - a_n| > \delta - \delta/2 = \delta/2.$$

Now let $(c_i)_i$ be the sequence of rational numbers defined by

$$c_i = 1 \quad \text{if } 1 \leqslant i < M,$$
$$a_i c_i = 1 \quad \text{if } i \geqslant M.$$

The choice of 1 for the first $M - 1$ terms of $(c_i)_i$ is quite arbitrary. The point is that if $1 \leqslant i < M$ then a_i may be 0, in which case $a_i x = 1$ is not solvable, but if $i \geqslant M$, then $a_i \neq 0$, so that $a_i x = 1$ has a solution.

We now show that $(c_i)_i$ is a Cauchy sequence. If $n \geqslant M$ and $m \geqslant M$, then

$$|a_n a_m| |c_n - c_m| = |a_n - a_m|$$

and $|a_n a_m| > \delta^2/4$, so that

$$|c_n - c_m| < (4/\delta^2)|a_n - a_m|.$$

The Cauchy property of $(c_i)_i$ now follows easily from the Cauchy property of $(a_i)_i$.

Since $(c_i)_i$ is a Cauchy sequence of rational numbers, $d = [(c_i)_i]$ is a real number. If $n \geqslant M$, then $|a_n c_n - 1| = 0$, so that $ad = [(1)_i]$. $\square$

The associative and commutative properties stated as (i), (ii), (iii), (iv) in the above theorem can be generalized to any finite number of terms by substituting 'real number' for 'integer' in the relevant parts of §7, Chapter 1. The reader is left to state and prove these results for himself. We will use them without further comment. We denote the real number x in (xi) by b/a.

Now we will embed **Q** in **R**. By the remarks in §4 of Chapter 1, we must find an injection f from **Q** to **R** such that $f(a+b)=f(a)+f(b)$ and $f(ab)=f(a)f(b)$ for all $a, b \in$ **Q**. If $a \in$ **Q**, then $[(a)_i]$ is just the set of those Cauchy sequences of rational numbers which have the limit a. This suggests that we consider the function f from **Q** to **R** defined by

$$f(a) = [(a)_i]$$

for all $a \in$ **Q**. This function satisfies the requirements:

(i) if $a, b \in$ **Q** and $f(a)=f(b)$, then $(a)_i \propto (b)_i$; that is, $|a-b| < \epsilon$ for every rational number $\epsilon > 0$, so that $a = b$;

(ii) if $a, b \in$ **Q**, then

$$f(a) + f(b) = [(a)_i] + [(b)_i] = [(a+b)_i] = f(a+b),$$

and similarly $f(a)f(b)=f(ab)$, by the definitions of the sum and product of two real numbers.

Thus **Q** can be embedded in **R** by replacing $[(a)_i]$ by a, for each $a \in$ **Q**.

It remains to be shown that every Cauchy sequence of rational numbers has a real number for its limit. In order to do this, we now consider the relation of inequality between real numbers.

DEFINITIONS. A real number a is *greater than* a real number b if $a \neq b$ and there are sequences $(a_i)_i$, $(b_i)_i$ in a, b, respectively, such that $a_n \geqslant b_n$ for all n. If a is greater than b then this is denoted by $a > b$. By b is *less than a*, denoted by $b < a$, we mean that a is greater than b. If $a > b$ or $a = b$, then this is denoted by $a \geqslant b$ or by $b \leqslant a$.

Since every rational number is a real number, the relation $a > b$ between rational numbers a, b has now been defined in two ways, once in the preceding section regarding them as rational numbers and now regarding them as real numbers. To show that these definitions are compatible, we note that:

(i) if $a > b$ (as rational numbers), then every term of the sequence $(a)_i$ is greater than every term of $(b)_i$, so that $a > b$ (as real numbers);

(ii) if $a > b$ (as real numbers) and $(a_i)_i$, $(b_i)_i$ are sequences as in the definition of $>$, then

$$b - a = (b - b_n) + (b_n - a_n) + (a_n - a)$$
$$\leqslant (b - b_n) + (a_n - a)$$

for all n. If $\epsilon > 0$ is a rational number, then n can be chosen so that $b - b_n$ and $a_n - a$ are both less than $\epsilon/2$ (as rational numbers), so that $b - a \leqslant 0$

— Exercise 6, p. 40 — and thus $a \geqslant b$ (as rational numbers). Also $a \neq b$, because $a > b$ (as real numbers), so that $a > b$ (as rational numbers).

THEOREM 4. *If a, b are real numbers, then*:
(i) *either $a > b$, $a < b$, or $a = b$;*
(ii) *if $a \geqslant b$ and $a \leqslant b$, then $a = b$;*
(iii) *if $a < b$, then there is a rational number c such that $a < c \leqslant b$;*
(iv) *if $a \neq 0$, then there is an integer n such that $b < na$.*

Proof. Let $a = [(a_i)_i]$ and $b = [(b_i)_i]$, and suppose that there is an integer N such that $a_n \geqslant b_n$ for all $n \geqslant N$. We then define the sequences $(a_i')_i$, $(b_i')_i$ by

$$a_n' = b_n' = 1 \qquad \text{if } 1 \leqslant n < N;$$
$$a_n' = a_n, \ b_n' = b_n \quad \text{if } n \geqslant N.$$

Obviously $a = [(a_i')_i]$ and $b = [(b_i')_i]$, so that $a \geqslant b$. Therefore, if $a \geqslant b$ does not hold, then there is no integer N with the above property. That is, if $a \geqslant b$ does not hold and N is an integer, then there is an integer $n \geqslant N$ such that $a_n < b_n$.

Now let $\epsilon > 0$ be a rational number. Since $(a_i)_i$ and $(b_i)_i$ are Cauchy sequences, there is an integer N such that $|a_n - a_m| < \epsilon/2$ and $|b_n - b_m| < \epsilon/2$ if $n \geqslant N$ and $m \geqslant N$. If $a \geqslant b$ does not hold, then there is an integer $s \geqslant N$ such that $a_s < b_s$. Thus, if $n \geqslant N$, then

$$a_n - b_n = (a_n - a_s) + (a_s - b_s) + (b_s - b_n) < \epsilon.$$

Similarly, if $b \geqslant a$ does not hold, then there is an integer M with the property: if $n \geqslant M$, then $b_n - a_n < \epsilon$. Therefore, if neither $a \geqslant b$ nor $b \geqslant a$ holds, then there is an integer R with the property: if $n \geqslant R$, then $|a_n - b_n| < \epsilon$. Thus $a = b$, and this proves (i).

If $a \leqslant b$ and $a \geqslant b$, then there are sequences $(a_i)_i$, $(a_i')_i$ in a and $(b_i)_i$, $(b_i')_i$ in b such that $a_n \leqslant b_n$ and $a_n' \geqslant b_n'$ for all n. Thus,

$$0 \leqslant b_n - a_n = (b_n - b_n') + (b_n' - a_n') + (a_n' - a_n)$$
$$\leqslant (b_n - b_n') + (a_n' - a_n)$$

for all n. Since $(b_i)_i \propto (b_i')_i$ and $(a_i)_i \propto (a_i')_i$, it follows from this inequality that $(b_i)_i \propto (a_i)_i$. This proves (ii).

We now prove (iii). If $a < b$, we can choose the sequences $(a_i)_i$, $(b_i)_i$ so that $a_n \leqslant b_n$ for all n. In the course of proving Theorem 3 we showed that, if $[(a_i)_i] \neq 0$, then there is a rational number $\delta > 0$ and an integer M with the property: if $n \geqslant M$, then $|a_n| > \delta/2$. Here $b - a \neq 0$, and so there is a rational number $\delta > 0$ and an integer M with the property: if $n \geqslant M$, then $|b_n - a_n| > \delta/2$. By our choice of sequences, $b_n - a_n \geqslant 0$ for all n, so that $b_n - a_n > \delta/2$ if $n \geqslant M$. Let N be an integer with the property: if $n \geqslant N$ and $m \geqslant N$, then $|a_n - a_m| < \delta/4$ and $|b_n - b_m| < \delta/4$. There is such an integer N because $(a_i)_i$ and $(b_i)_i$ are Cauchy sequences. If $m \geqslant N$ and n is larger than N and M, then

$$a_m < a_n + \delta/4 < b_n - \delta/4 < b_m.$$

From these inequalities it easily follows that

$$a \leqslant a_n + \delta/4 < b_n - \delta/4 \leqslant b,$$

and since $b_n - \delta/4$ is a rational number, this proves (iii).

In order to simplify the proof of (iv), we assume the results of Exercises 3, 4 below. If $0 \leqslant |b| < |a|$, then $b < na$ where $n = 1$ or -1. If $0 < |a| \leqslant |b|$, then there are rational numbers c, d such that $0 < c \leqslant |a|$ and $|b| < d \leqslant |b| + 1$, and, by Theorem 2, there is an integer $n > 0$ such that $d < nc$. By Exercises 3, 4,

$$b < d < nc \leqslant n|a| = (\pm n)a. \quad \square$$

EXERCISES

1. Prove that, for all real numbers a, b, (i) $-(-a) = a$; (ii) $0a = 0$; (iii) $a(-b) = -(ab)$; (iv) $(-a)(-b) = ab$.

2. Show that, if a, b, c are real numbers such that $a + b = a + c$, then $b = c$.

3. Show that, if a, b, c are real numbers such that $a < b$, then:
(i) $a + c < b + c$;
(ii) if $0 < c$, then $ac < bc$; if $0 > c$, then $ac > bc$;
(iii) if $b < c$, then $a < c$;
(iv) $a < (1/2)(a + b) < b$;
(v) $0 \leqslant c^2$, and $0 = c^2$ if and only if $c = 0$.

4. Define the *absolute value*, $|a|$, of a real number a to be a if $a \geqslant 0$ and $-a$ if $a < 0$. Show that for every rational number this definition agrees with that given in Exercise 7, p. 40, and that for all real numbers a, b, c:
(i) $|a + b| \leqslant |a| + |b|$;
(ii) $|a - b| \leqslant |a - c| + |c - b|$;
(iii) $|ab| = |a||b|$.

5. Let a be a real number such that $a \leqslant b$ for every rational number $b > 0$. Show that $a \leqslant 0$.

6. Let $a = [(a_i)_i]$ and $b = [(b_i)_i]$ be real numbers such that $a < b$. Show that there is an integer N such that, for all $n \geqslant N$, $a_n < b$, $b_n > a$, and $a_n < b_n$.

7. Show that, if $(a_i)_i$ is a Cauchy sequence of rational numbers, then $(|a_i|)_i$ is also a Cauchy sequence and $|[(a_i)_i]| = [(|a_i|)_i]$.

8. Let a be a real number, $a > 1$. Show that

$$a^n \geqslant 1 + n(a - 1)$$

for all positive integers n. Let b be a real number. Show that there is an integer n such that $a^n \geqslant b$.

3   Sequences of real numbers

DEFINITIONS. A *Cauchy sequence of real numbers* is an infinite sequence $(a_i)_i$ of real numbers with the property: with each real number $\epsilon > 0$ there can be associated an integer N such that $|a_n - a_m| < \epsilon$ if $n \geqslant N$ and $m \geqslant N$.

A real number a is the *limit* of an infinite sequence $(a_i)_i$ of real numbers if it has the property: with each real number $\epsilon > 0$ there can be associated an integer N such that $|a - a_n| < \epsilon$ whenever $n \geqslant N$. If a is the limit of $(a_i)_i$, then $(a_i)_i$ is said to *converge* to a.

In §2 we defined the term 'Cauchy sequence of rational numbers'. Suppose that $(a_i)_i$ is such a sequence. Then it is a sequence of real numbers, since every rational number is a real number. Let $\epsilon > 0$ be a real number. By Theorem 4(iii) there is a rational number δ such that $0 < \delta \leqslant \epsilon$, and since $(a_i)_i$ is a Cauchy sequence of rational numbers there is an integer N with the property: if $n \geqslant N$ and $m \geqslant N$, then $|a_n - a_m| < \delta$. Therefore, if $n \geqslant N$ and $m \geqslant N$, then $|a_n - a_m| < \epsilon$. Thus, a Cauchy sequence of rational numbers is a Cauchy sequence of real numbers. Similarly, if a rational number a is the limit of a sequence $(a_i)_i$ of rational numbers, then a is the limit of the sequence $(a_i)_i$ in the sense of the above definition.

THEOREM 5. *A convergent sequence of real numbers is a Cauchy sequence, and it has only one limit.*

Proof. Let $(a_i)_i$ be a sequence of real numbers with limit a, and let $\epsilon > 0$ be a real number. Let N be an integer with the property: if $n \geqslant N$, then $|a_n - a| < \epsilon/2$. If $n \geqslant N$ and $m \geqslant N$, then

$$|a_n - a_m| \leqslant |a_n - a| + |a - a_m| < \epsilon,$$

so that $(a_i)_i$ is a Cauchy sequence. If b is the limit of $(a_i)_i$, then there is an integer M with the property: if $n \geqslant M$, then $|a_n - b| < \epsilon/2$. Let n be an integer such that $n \geqslant N$ and $n \geqslant M$. Then

$$|a - b| \leqslant |a - a_n| + |a_n - b| < \epsilon,$$

so that $|a - b| = 0$, and thus $a = b$. $\square$

THEOREM 6. *A real number a is the limit of a Cauchy sequence $(a_i)_i$ of rational numbers if and only if $a = [(a_i)_i]$.*

Proof. Suppose that $(a_i)_i$ is a Cauchy sequence of rational numbers. We must show that $a = [(a_i)_i]$ is the limit of $(a_i)_i$. Let $\epsilon > 0$ be a real number, and let δ be a rational number such that $0 < \delta \leqslant \epsilon$. Since $(a_i)_i$ is a Cauchy sequence, there is an integer N with the property: if $n \geqslant N$ and $m \geqslant N$, then $a_n - \delta < a_m < a_n + \delta$. From this, and the definition of $<$, it easily follows that $a - \delta \leqslant a_m \leqslant a + \delta$ for all $m \geqslant N$, so that $|a - a_m| \leqslant \delta \leqslant \epsilon$ for these m. Thus a is the limit of the sequence $(a_i)_i$.

Now suppose that a real number a is the limit of a sequence $(a_i)_i$ of rational numbers, and let $a = [(c_i)_i]$. Let $\epsilon > 0$ be a real number. Since a is the limit of $(a_i)_i$, there is an integer N with the property: if $n \geqslant N$, then $|a - a_n| < \epsilon/2$. By the first part of this theorem, a is the limit of $(c_i)_i$, so there is an integer M with the property: if $n \geqslant M$, then $|a - c_n| < \epsilon/2$. Let R be the larger of N, M. If $n \geqslant R$, then $|c_n - a_n| < \epsilon$, and it follows from the definition of real number that $a = [(a_i)_i]$. $\square$

THEOREM 7. *Every Cauchy sequence of real numbers is convergent.*

Proof. Let $(a_i)_i$ be a Cauchy sequence of real numbers, and let $a_i = [(b_j^i)_j]$, where $(b_j^i)_j$ is a Cauchy sequence of rational numbers. That is, b_j^i is the j-th term in a sequence of rational numbers which defines the real number a_i. By the preceding theorem there is, for each i, an integer $j(i)$ such that $|a_i - b_{j(i)}^i| < 1/i$. (In fact, all but a finite number of integers could have been chosen to be $j(i)$.) We will now show that $(b_{j(i)}^i)_i$ is a Cauchy sequence, and that $[(b_{j(i)}^i)_i]$ is the limit of $(a_i)_i$.

Let $\epsilon > 0$ be a real number, and let N be an integer with the property: if $n \geqslant N$ and $m \geqslant N$, then $1/n < \epsilon/3$ and $|a_n - a_m| < \epsilon/3$. There is such an integer N because $(a_i)_i$ is a Cauchy sequence. If $n \geqslant N$ and $m \geqslant N$, then

$$
\begin{aligned}
|b_{j(n)}^n - b_{j(m)}^m| &\leqslant |b_{j(n)}^n - a_n| + |a_m - b_{j(m)}^m| + |a_n - a_m| \\
&< 1/n + 1/m + |a_n - a_m| \\
&< \epsilon,
\end{aligned}
$$

so that $(b_{j(i)}^i)_i$ is a Cauchy sequence of rational numbers. If $n \geqslant N$, then

$$
\begin{aligned}
|a_n - [(b_{j(i)}^i)_i]| &\leqslant |a_n - b_{j(n)}^n| + |b_{j(n)}^n - [(b_{j(i)}^i)_i]| \\
&< \epsilon/3 + |b_{j(n)}^n - [(b_{j(i)}^i)_i]|.
\end{aligned}
$$

By the preceding theorem, there is an integer R with the property: if $n \geqslant R$, then $|b_{j(n)}^n - [(b_{j(i)}^i)_i]| < 2\epsilon/3$. Therefore, if $n \geqslant N$ and $n \geqslant R$, then

$$
|a_n - [(b_{j(i)}^i)_i]| < \epsilon,
$$

so that $(a_i)_i$ has the limit $[(b_{j(i)}^i)_i]$. $\square$

Theorems 3 and 7 show that the set of real numbers has the properties that we anticipated in §2. Further development of the theory of real numbers can be found in any textbook on real analysis and we conclude with a theorem which is sometimes taken as a postulate in such books.

DEFINITIONS. A real number a is a *lower bound* for a set A of real numbers if $b \geqslant a$ for all $b \in A$. If A has a lower bound, then A is *bounded below*. A real number a is the *greatest lower bound* for A if it is a lower bound which is greater than all other lower bounds for A.

THEOREM 8. *Every non-empty set of real numbers which is bounded below has a greatest lower bound.*

Proof. Let A be a non-empty set of real numbers with a lower bound a, and let $\epsilon > 0$ be a real number. By Theorem 4(iv), p. 47, and the well-ordering theorem for the positive integers, p. 15, there is an integer n such that $a + n\epsilon$ is a lower bound for A but $a + (n+1)\epsilon$ is not a lower bound for A. Let $a(\epsilon) = a + n\epsilon$. The sequence $(a(1/i))_i$ is a Cauchy sequence since $|a(1/n) - a(1/m)|$ is less than the larger of $1/n$, $1/m$, and so it has a limit which is easily seen to be the greatest lower bound for A. □

This theorem is similar to the well-ordering theorem for the positive integers, but we note that a set of real numbers need not contain its greatest lower bound. For example, the set of real numbers greater than 0 does not contain its greatest lower bound, which is 0.

EXERCISES

1. A set A of real numbers is *open* if, with each $a \in A$ there can be associated a real number $\delta > 0$ with the property: if b is a real number such that $|a - b| < \delta$, then $b \in A$. Show that:
(i) for any real numbers a, b, the set $\{x \mid a < x < b\}$ is open;
(ii) the empty set and the set of all real numbers are open;
(iii) if A and $\{x \mid x \in \mathbf{R} \text{ and } x \notin A\}$ are both open, then one of them is empty. [If $a \in A$, $b \notin A$, and $a < b$, then the set $\{x \mid x \notin A \text{ and } x > a\}$ cannot have a greatest lower bound, contrary to the result of Theorem 8.]

2. A function f from the set of all real numbers to that set is *continuous* if, with each ordered pair $\langle a, \epsilon \rangle$ of real numbers such that $\epsilon > 0$ there can be associated a real number $\delta > 0$ with the property: if b is a real number such that $|a - b| < \delta$, then $|f(a) - f(b)| < \epsilon$. Show that:
(i) f is continuous if and only if the set $\{x \mid f(x) \in A\}$ is open for all open sets A;
(ii) if f is continuous and there are real numbers a, b, c such that $f(a) < b < f(c)$, then there is a real number d such that $f(d) = b$. [The set $\{x \mid f(x) > b\}$ cannot be the complement of $\{x \mid f(x) < b\}$, by (i) and Exercise 1(iii).]

3. Show that the function f defined by $f(x) = x^n$, where n is a positive integer, is continuous. Let $a > 0$ be a real number. Show that there is a unique real number $\sqrt[n]{a} > 0$ such that $(\sqrt[n]{a})^n = a$.

4. An infinite sequence $(a_i)_i$ of real numbers has the properties:
(i) $a_{n+1} \leqslant a_n$ for all n;
(ii) the set $\{a_1, a_2, a_3, \ldots\}$ is bounded below.
Show that $(a_i)_i$ converges to the greatest lower bound of the set $\{a_1, a_2, a_3, \ldots\}$.

5. A real number a is an *upper bound* for a set A of real numbers if $b \leqslant a$ for all $b \in A$. If A has an upper bound, then A is *bounded above*. A real number a is the *least upper bound* for A if it is an upper bound which is less than all other

upper bounds for A. Show that every non-empty set of real numbers which is bounded above has a least upper bound.

4   Three inequalities between real numbers

In this section we prove three inequalities which are of some use in elementary analysis and algebra.

DEFINITION. A real number a is *positive* if $a > 0$.

(i) Weierstrass's Inequality. *If $a_1, a_2, a_3, \ldots, a_n$ are positive real numbers, then*

$$\prod_{i=1}^{n} (1 + a_i) \geqslant 1 + \sum_{i=1}^{n} a_i.$$

Proof. We proceed by induction on n. The inequality is trivial if $n = 1$. If it holds for $n = m$, then

$$\prod_{i=1}^{m+1} (1 + a_i) = (1 + a_{m+1})\left(\prod_{i=1}^{m} (1 + a_i) \right)$$

$$= \prod_{i=1}^{m} (1 + a_i) + a_{m+1}\left(\prod_{i=1}^{m} (1 + a_i) \right)$$

$$\geqslant \left(1 + \sum_{i=1}^{m} a_i\right) + a_{m+1},$$

which, by the principle of induction, proves the required result. □

(ii) Cauchy's Inequality. *If $a_1, a_2, a_3, \ldots, a_n, b_1, b_2, b_3, \ldots, b_n$ are real numbers, then*

$$\left(\sum_{i=1}^{n} a_i b_i \right)^2 \leqslant \left(\sum_{i=1}^{n} a_i^2 \right)\left(\sum_{i=1}^{n} b_i^2 \right),$$

and equality occurs if and only if $a_i b_j = a_j b_i$ for all $i, j = 1, 2, 3, \ldots, n$.

Proof. This follows immediately from the inequality

$$\left(\sum_{i=1}^{n} a_i^2 \right)\left(\sum_{i=1}^{n} b_i^2 \right) - \left(\sum_{i=1}^{n} a_i b_i \right)^2 = \sum_{i=1}^{n}\left(\sum_{j=1}^{n} (a_i b_j - a_j b_i)^2 / 2 \right) \geqslant 0,$$

which is easily proved by induction. □

DEFINITIONS. The *arithmetic mean* or *average* of the n positive real numbers $a_1, a_2, a_3, \ldots, a_n$ is $(a_1 + a_2 + a_3 + \ldots + a_n)/n$, and their *geometric mean* is $\sqrt[n]{(a_1 a_2 a_3 \ldots a_n)}$.

The real number $\sqrt[n]{a}$ was defined in Exercise 3, p. 51, for all $a > 0$. The numbers $a_1, a_2, a_3, \ldots, a_n$ must obviously be regarded as constituting a finite sequence in computing their arithmetic or geometric means, but we will refer to $a_1, a_2, a_3, \ldots, a_n$ as a set, in accordance with common usage, since the values obtained for the means are independent of the order in which the n numbers are taken.

(iii) The Theorem of the Means. *If A and G are respectively the arithmetic and geometric means of the n positive real numbers $a_1, a_2, a_3, \ldots, a_n$, then $A \geqslant G$; and $A = G$ if and only if these n numbers are all equal.*

Proof. It is clear that, if all the a_i are equal, then $A = G$, so we need only show that, if not all the a_i are equal, then $A > G$.

Let R_1 be a set of not-all-equal positive real numbers $a_1, a_2, a_3, \ldots, a_n$ with arithmetic mean A and geometric mean G_1. The set R_1 contains real numbers (which, by a change of subscript, can be taken to be a_1, a_2) such that $a_1 < A < a_2$. Let R_2 be the set $A, a_1 + a_2 - A, a_3, a_4, \ldots, a_n$. The arithmetic mean of R_2 is A, the same as that of R_1. Let G_2 be the geometric mean of R_2. Since $A > a_1 > 0$ and $a_1 + a_2 - A > a_1 > 0$, these means exist and we have

$$
\begin{aligned}
G_2^n - G_1^n &= (a_3 a_4 a_5 \ldots a_n)(A(a_1 + a_2 - A) - a_1 a_2) \\
&= (a_3 a_4 a_5 \ldots a_n)(A - a_1)(a_2 - A) \\
&> 0,
\end{aligned}
$$

so that $G_2 > G_1$. If the real numbers in R_2 are all equal, then $A = G_2 > G_1$, and the theorem is proved. If the real numbers in R_2 are not all equal, then the above procedure can be repeated to obtain a set R_3 with arithmetic mean A and geometric mean G_3, and so on. The important point to note is that at each step two real numbers, neither of which is A, are replaced, one of them by A. Thus, at each step the number of terms equal to A increases, and so after at most $n - 1$ steps we achieve a set of equal real numbers. That is, for some integer $m \leqslant n - 1$, all the members of R_m are equal to A, so that $A = G_m > G_{m-1} > G_{m-2} \ldots > G_1$. □

EXERCISES

1. Show that, if a, b, c, d are positive real numbers, then:
(i) $a^2 + b^2 \geqslant 2ab$;
(ii) $a^3 + b^3 + c^3 \geqslant 3abc$;
(iii) $a^4 + b^4 + c^4 + d^4 \geqslant 4abcd$;
(iv) if $a + b + c = 6$, then $ab^2 c^3 \leqslant 108$;
(v) if $1/a + 1/b + 1/c = 1$, then $(a - 1)(b - 1)(c - 1) \geqslant 8$.

2. Show that, if n positive real numbers have the sum nx, then their product is not greater than x^n and the sum of their squares is between nx^2 and $n^2 x^2$.

3. By applying the theorem of the means to the set consisting of $(n^2 - 1)/n^2$ taken n times and $(n + 1)/n$ taken once, show that, for all positive integers n,
$$(1 - 1/n)^n < (1 - 1/(n + 1))^{n+1}.$$

4. If a, b, c are positive real numbers such that
$$1/3 \leqslant ab + bc + ca \leqslant 3,$$
find the range of possible values of abc and $a + b + c$.

5. Show, by an example, that the following is not a proof of the theorem of the means: Assuming that at least two of the real numbers $a_1, a_2, a_3, \ldots, a_n$ are not equal, let them be a_1 and a_2, and consider the set
$$(a_1 + a_2)/2, \ (a_1 + a_2)/2, \ a_3, \ a_4, \ldots, a_n.$$
This set has the same arithmetic mean as the original set but its geometric mean is larger since $(a_1 + a_2)^2 > 4a_1 a_2$. Repeat this until a set is obtained which has all its elements equal and thus prove the theorem.

6. Show that, if a, b, c are positive real numbers and $a \neq b$, then:
(i) $a^3 b + ab^3 < a^4 + b^4$;
(ii) $(a^2 + b^2 + c^2)^2 < (a + b + c)(a^3 + b^3 + c^3)$.

7. Find those real numbers x such that
$$(x - 1)/(x^2 - x - 12) < 1/(x + 2).$$

5   The complex numbers

If x is a real number, then $x^2 \geqslant 0$. Thus there is no real number x such that $x^2 = -1$. We will now embed **R** in a set **C** which has all the algebraic properties of **R** as expressed in Theorem 3, p. 44, and which contains a solution to $x^2 = -1$.

Suppose, for the moment, that we have obtained such a set **C**, and let i be an element of **C** such that $i^2 = -1$. If a, b are real numbers, then $a + ib \in$ **C**, since **R** $\subseteq$ **C** and the sum and product of any two elements of **C** are in **C**. Thus, every ordered pair $\langle a, b \rangle$ of real numbers can be associated with an element $a + ib \in$ **C**. Suppose that two such ordered pairs $\langle a, b \rangle$, $\langle c, d \rangle$ are associated in this way with the same element of **C**, that is, suppose that a, b, c, d are real numbers such that $a + ib = c + id$. Then $a - c = i(b - d)$, so that $(a - c)^2 = -(b - d)^2$. But a, b, c, d are real numbers and so, by the first remark of this section, $a = c$ and $b = d$. That is, the element $a + ib$ determines a unique ordered pair $\langle a, b \rangle$. Now let a, b, c, d be any real numbers. By the commutative, associative, and distributive laws, the sum of $a + ib$ and $c + id$ is
$$(a + ib) + (c + id) = (a + c) + i(b + d),$$
and their product is
$$(a + ib)(c + id) = ac + i^2 bd + i(bc + ad)$$
$$= (ac - bd) + i(bc + ad).$$

DEFINITIONS. A *complex number* is an ordered pair of real numbers. The set of all complex numbers is denoted by **C**. The *sum* $\langle a, b \rangle + \langle c, d \rangle$

of the complex numbers $\langle a, b \rangle$, $\langle c, d \rangle$ is the complex number $\langle a + c, \ b + d \rangle$ and their *product* $\langle a, b \rangle \langle c, d \rangle$ is $\langle ac - bd, \ bc + ad \rangle$. The complex number $\langle -a, -b \rangle$ is denoted by $-\langle a, b \rangle$, and the sum $n + (-m)$ of the complex numbers $n, -m$ is denoted by $n - m$. Sometimes we will denote the product nm by $n \cdot m$. The complex number $\langle 0, 1 \rangle$ is denoted by i.

Clearly, the sum and product of two complex numbers n, m are complex numbers which are uniquely determined by the ordered pair $\langle n, m \rangle$.

THEOREM 9. *If a, b, c are complex numbers, then*:

(i) $(a + b) + c = a + (b + c)$;

(ii) $(ab)c = a(bc)$;

(iii) $a + b = b + a$;

(iv) $ab = ba$;

(v) $a + \langle 0, 0 \rangle = a$;

(vi) $a \langle 1, 0 \rangle = a$;

(vii) $a(b + c) = ab + ac$;

(viii) $a - a = \langle 0, 0 \rangle$;

(ix) *if* $ab = ac$ *and* $a \neq \langle 0, 0 \rangle$, *then* $b = c$;

(x) *there is one and only one complex number x such that* $a + x = b$; *it is* $b - a$;

(xi) *if* $a \neq \langle 0, 0 \rangle$, *then there is one and only one complex number x such that* $ax = b$.

Proof. These results follow easily from the definitions and Theorem 3. For example, to prove (xi) we first note, as in the proof of Theorem 3(xi), that it is sufficient to show that there is a complex number x such that $ax = \langle 1, 0 \rangle$. Let $a = \langle e, f \rangle$. Then a straightforward calculation shows that $x = \langle e/e^2 + f^2, -f/e^2 + f^2 \rangle$ is a solution to $ax = \langle 1, \ 0 \rangle$. We note that x exists, since at least one of e, f is non-0, so that $e^2 + f^2 \neq 0$.

The proof of the remaining results is left to the reader. □

The associative and commutative properties stated as (i), (ii), (iii), (iv) in the above theorem can be generalized to any finite number of terms by suitably modifying the relevant parts of §7, Chapter 1. In particular, a^n is defined, for all $a \in \mathbf{C}$ and all positive integers n, by the relations $a^1 = a$, $a^n = a^{n-1} a$. Also, the unique solution to $ax = b$, where $a, b \in \mathbf{C}$ and $a \neq 0$, will be denoted by b/a. The existence and uniqueness of b/a has been proved in (xi) above.

In order to embed $\mathbf{R}$ in $\mathbf{C}$, we must find an injection f from $\mathbf{R}$ to $\mathbf{C}$ such that

$$f(a + b) = f(a) + f(b)$$

and
$$f(ab) = f(a) f(b)$$

for all $a, b \in \mathbf{R}$. It is easily seen that the function f defined by

$$f(a) = \langle a, 0 \rangle$$

for all $a \in \mathbf{R}$ is such an injection. Therefore, by the remarks in §4 of Chapter 1, $\mathbf{R}$ can be embedded in $\mathbf{C}$ by replacing $\langle a, 0 \rangle$ by a, for each $a \in \mathbf{R}$. We will now regard the real number a and the complex number $\langle a, 0 \rangle$ as identical, so that $\mathbf{R}$ is now a subset of $\mathbf{C}$. It only remains to find an element $x \in \mathbf{C}$ such that $x^2 = -1$; the complex number $i = (0, 1)$ is such an element since $(0, 1)^2 = (-1, 0) = -1$. We have therefore constructed a set $\mathbf{C}$ with the properties that we anticipated at the beginning of this section.

It would now be natural to consider extending $\mathbf{C}$ to a set which contains a solution to, say, $x^2 = i$, or to some similar equation. In fact, this is not necessary, since $\mathbf{C}$ contains solutions to all equations of this type. It can be shown that, *if $a_1, a_2, a_3, \ldots, a_n$ is a finite sequence of complex numbers, if $a_n \neq 0$, and if $n > 1$, then there is a complex number z such that*

$$a_1 + a_2 z + a_3 z^2 + \ldots + a_n z^{n-1} = 0.$$

This result is called the *Fundamental Theorem of Algebra* and its proof can be found in any book on complex analysis.[1]

We note that a complex number $\langle a, b \rangle$ can be written

$$\begin{aligned} \langle a, b \rangle &= \langle a, 0 \rangle + \langle 0, b \rangle \\ &= \langle a, 0 \rangle + \langle 0, 1 \rangle \langle b, 0 \rangle \\ &= a + ib. \end{aligned}$$

This way of expressing $\langle a, b \rangle$ was anticipated at the beginning of this section. If complex numbers are expressed in this way, then calculations with them can be performed using only the results of Theorem 9 and the fact that $i^2 = -1$. The rather complicated definitions of 'sum' and 'product' need not be remembered, though, of course, they were essential in the construction of $\mathbf{C}$.

EXERCISES

1. Prove that, for all complex numbers a, b, (i) $-(-a) = a$; (ii) $0a = 0$; (iii) $a(-b) = -(ab)$; (iv) $(-a)(-b) = ab$.

2. Let a, b be real numbers, $a \neq 0$. Show that $-b$ and b/a, as defined on p. 55, are the real numbers as defined on p. 43 and p. 46.

---

[1] Simple proofs can be found in Weisner, *Theory of Equations* (New York, 1938), pp. 145–149, and Rudin, *Principles of Mathematical Analysis*, Second Edition (New York, 1964), p. 170.

3. The *conjugate*, $\overline{\langle a, b \rangle}$, of the complex number $\langle a, b \rangle$ is defined to be $\langle a, -b \rangle$. Let c, d be complex numbers. Show that

$$\overline{c + d} = \bar{c} + \bar{d}$$

and

$$\overline{cd} = \bar{c}\,\bar{d},$$

and generalize these results to any finite sequence of complex numbers.

4. The *absolute value* $|\langle a, b \rangle|$ of the complex number $\langle a, b \rangle$ is defined to be $\sqrt[2]{(a^2 + b^2)}$. Show that, if $\langle a, b \rangle$ is a real number, then this definition agrees with that given in Exercise 4, p. 48. Let a_1, a_2, $a_3, \ldots, a_n$ be a finite sequence of complex numbers. Show that:

(i) $\left| \sum_{i=1}^{n} a_i \right| \leqslant \sum_{i=1}^{n} |a_i|$;

(ii) $\left| \prod_{i=1}^{n} a_i \right| = \prod_{i=1}^{n} |a_i|$.

5. Let a be a complex number. Show that $a\bar{a} = |a|^2$ and that, if $a \neq 0$, then $1/a = \bar{a}/|a|^2$.

6. Show that, for any two complex numbers a, b,
$$|1 - a\bar{b}|^2 - |a - b|^2 = (1 - |a|^2)(1 - |b|^2).$$

7. Prove that, if a, b are complex numbers and c is a positive real number, then

$$|a + b|^2 \leqslant (1 + c)|a|^2 + (1 + 1/c)|b|^2.$$

Under what conditions does the relation of equality hold?
Prove also that if z_1, z_2, $z_3, \ldots, z_n$ are complex numbers, and a_1, a_2, $a_3, \ldots, a_n$ are positive real numbers such that $1/a_1 + 1/a_2 + 1/a_3 + \ldots + 1/a_n = 1$, then

$$|z_1 + z_2 + z_3 + \ldots + z_n|^2 \leqslant a_1 |z_1|^2 + a_2 |z_2|^2 + a_3 |z_3|^2 + \ldots + a_n |z_n|^2.$$

8. Show that, if a_1, a_2, $a_3, \ldots, a_n$ are complex numbers such that $|a_i| < 2$ for all $i = 1, 2, 3, \ldots, n$, then the equation

$$1 + a_1 z + a_2 z^2 + a_3 z^3 + \ldots + a_n z^n = 0$$

has no solution z such that $|z| < 1/3$.

9. Let z_1, z_2, $z_3, \ldots, z_n$ be complex numbers, and let
$$y = (z_1 + z_2 + z_3 + \ldots + z_n)/n.$$
Prove that, for any complex number z,

$$\sum_{i=1}^{n} |z - z_i|^2 \geqslant n|z - y|^2.$$

Under what circumstances is equality possible?

10. A *Cauchy sequence of complex numbers* is an infinite sequence $(a_i)_i$ of complex numbers with the property: with each real number $\epsilon > 0$ there can be associated an integer N such that $|a_n - a_m| < \epsilon$ if $n \geqslant N$ and $m \geqslant N$. A complex number a

5

is the *limit* of an infinite sequence $(a_i)_i$ of complex numbers if with each real number $\epsilon > 0$ there can be associated an integer N such that $|a - a_n| < \epsilon$ if $n \geqslant N$. Show that every Cauchy sequence of complex numbers has a limit.

6 The geometry of the complex numbers

In this section we use geometrical terms like 'point', 'line', and 'plane' without defining them, and we will rely on intuition to suggest their properties. The set **R** of real numbers is commonly represented as a straight line by associating 0 and 1 with two different points on a line and then associating $x \in$ **R** with the point which is at a distance $|x|$ from 0 and is on the same side of 0 as 1 if and only if $x > 0$. If two perpendicular straight lines are fixed in a plane, then each point of the plane is uniquely determined by its projections on to these lines. Thus, each point of the plane can be associated with an ordered pair of real numbers, that is, with a complex number. Since every complex number is obviously the associate of a point of the plane, the set **C** of complex numbers can be represented by a plane. Thus, we sometimes refer to a complex number z as the *point z*. Also, we can associate the line segment from 0 to z with the complex number z. This line segment will be referred to as the *vector z*.

It is interesting to note that the complex numbers were first used in 1545, in order to solve the cubic equation, but it was not until 1673 that John Wallis suggested that they could be represented by points in the plane.

Since every complex number can be regarded as a point, every relationship between complex numbers can be interpreted geometrically as a relationship between points. For example:

(i) The sum of the complex numbers $y = \langle a, b \rangle$, $z = \langle c, d \rangle$ is associated with the vector $\langle a + c, b + d \rangle$, which is a diagonal of the parallelogram with the vectors y, z as two adjacent sides.

(ii) If a complex number z is multiplied by a positive real number c, then the point cz lies on the line from 0 through z and at a distance $c|z|$ from 0.

(iii) The distance from the point 0 to the point z is $|z|$, by Pythagoras's theorem. A triangle with vertices 0, y, $y + z$, has sides of length $|y|$, $|z|$, $|y + z|$, so the inequality

$$|y + z| \leqslant |y| + |z|$$

just expresses the geometric result: the length of a side of a triangle is not greater than the sum of the lengths of the other two sides. The more general inequality set as Exercise 4(i), p. 57, expresses a similar fact about polygons.

In order to interpret the product of two complex numbers geometrically, we assume some of the elementary properties of the sine and cosine functions.

DEFINITIONS. Let $z = \langle a, b \rangle$ be a complex number. The *argument* or *amplitude* of z, denoted by arg z, is any real number α such that $a = |z| \cos \alpha$ and $b = |z| \sin \alpha$. The numbers $|z|$, arg z are the *polar coordinates* of z.

Every complex number z can be written

$$z = a + ib$$
$$= |z| \left(\cos(\arg z) + i \sin(\arg z) \right).$$

If z is expressed in this way, then it is said to be in *polar form*. The polar coordinates of z are easily interpreted geometrically: $|z|$ is the distance from 0 to z, and arg z is the angle between the vectors 1 and z. Clearly, arg z is not uniquely determined by z.

Let y, z be two complex numbers. In polar form, they are

$$y = |y| \left(\cos(\arg y) + i \sin(\arg y) \right)$$

and
$$z = |z| \left(\cos(\arg z) + i \sin(\arg z) \right),$$

so that

$$yz = |y|\,|z| \left(\cos(\arg y) \cos(\arg z) - \sin(\arg y) \sin(\arg z) \right.$$
$$\left. + i(\sin(\arg y) \cos(\arg z) + \cos(\arg y) \sin(\arg z)) \right)$$

$$= |y|\,|z| \left(\cos(\arg y + \arg z) + i \sin(\arg y + \arg z) \right).$$

In the last step above we used the addition formulae for sine and cosine. We have shown that arg yz can be taken to be arg y + arg z; and thus, to find the point yz, we first rotate y by arg z to obtain

$$|y| \left(\cos(\arg yz) + i \sin(\arg yz) \right)$$

and then multiply this by $|z|$, as in (ii) above, to obtain yz.

EXERCISES

1. Express the following complex numbers in polar form:
$1 + i$, $1 + i\sqrt{3}$, $(1 + i\sqrt{3})/(1 + i)$, $1 + \cos(\pi/4) + i \sin(\pi/4)$, $(2 + 2i)^8$.

2. Show geometrically that, if z is a complex number such that $0 \leqslant \arg z \leqslant \pi$, and $z + |z| \neq 0$, then:
(i) $\arg(z + |z|) = (\arg z)/2$;
(ii) $\arg((z - |z|)/(z + |z|)) = \pi/2$;
(iii) $(z - |z|)/(z + |z|) = i \tan((\arg z)/2)$.

3. Show that, for any two complex numbers y, z,
$$|y + z|^2 + |y - z|^2 = 2(|y|^2 + |z|^2),$$
and interpret this result geometrically.

4. Show that the complex numbers x, y, z are the vertices of an equilateral triangle if and only if

$$x^2 + y^2 + z^2 = xy + yz + zx.$$

7 The roots of unity

Let z be a complex number, written in polar form

$$z = |z| \, (\cos \alpha + i \sin \alpha).$$

Since $|z^2| = |z|^2$, and $\arg z^2$ can be taken to be $2 \arg z$, we have

$$z^2 = |z|^2 (\cos 2\alpha + i \sin 2\alpha).$$

This is easily generalized, by induction on n, to

$$z^n = |z|^n (\cos n\alpha + i \sin n\alpha)$$

for all positive integers n. This result is called 'Demoivre's formula'. We will now use it to find the solutions to $x^n = 1$.

DEFINITION. Let n be a positive integer. A complex number z is an *n-th root of unity* if $z^n = 1$.

If z is an n-th root of unity, then

$$1 = z^n = |z|^n (\cos n\alpha + i \sin n\alpha),$$

from which it follows that $|z|^n = 1$ and that $n\alpha$ is an integral multiple of 2π. Since $|z| \geqslant 0$, $|z|$ must be 1. Thus,

$$z = \cos (2\pi m/n) + i \sin (2\pi m/n)$$

for some integer m. Conversely, if z is of this form then

$$z^n = \cos (2\pi m) + i \sin (2\pi m) = 1,$$

so that z is an n-th root of unity. Therefore, the n-th roots of unity are those complex numbers which are of the form

$$\cos (2\pi m/n) + i \sin (2\pi m/n),$$

where m is an integer.

Consider a typical n-th root

$$\cos (2\pi m/n) + i \sin (2\pi m/n).$$

Since $n > 0$, there are integers q, r such that $m = nq + r$ and $0 \leqslant r < n$. Thus,

$$2\pi m/n = 2\pi q + 2\pi r/n,$$

where q, r are integers and $0 \leqslant r < n$, so the n-th roots of unity are those complex numbers which are of the form

$$\cos (2\pi r/n) + i \sin (2\pi r/n)$$

where $0 \leqslant r < n$. These n numbers are all different, because no two of them have arguments differing by a multiple of 2π. Therefore, there are exactly n n-th roots of unity and they are

$$1, \beta, \beta^2, \ldots, \beta^{n-1},$$

where $\beta = \cos(2\pi/n) + i\sin(2\pi/n)$.

DEFINITION. A *primitive n-th root of unity* is an n-th root of unity z with the property: if $0 < m < n$, then z is not an m-th root of unity.

Every n-th root of unity is a primitive m-th root of unity, where m is the smallest integer in the set $\{s \mid z \text{ is an } s\text{-th root of unity}\}$. The only primitive 1-st root is 1, the only primitive square root is -1, and the primitive 4-th roots are i and $-i$. For each positive integer n,

$$\beta = \cos(2\pi/n) + i\sin(2\pi/n)$$

is a primitive n-th root, because $\arg(\beta^m) = 2\pi m/n$ is a multiple of 2π if and only if n divides m. This is a special case of the following theorem.

THEOREM 10. *If z is a primitive n-th root of unity and is also an m-th root of unity, then n divides m. If z is an n-th root of unity and n divides m, then z is an m-th root of unity.*

Proof. Let z be both a primitive n-th root and an m-th root, and let q, r be integers such that $m = nq + r$ and $0 \leqslant r < n$. Then

$$1 = z^m = z^{nq+r} = (z^n)^q z^r = z^r.$$

Since z is a primitive n-th root, $z^r \neq 1$ if $0 < r < n$. Thus $r = 0$, so that n divides m.

The second part follows from

$$z^m = z^{ns} = (z^n)^s = 1,$$

where $s = m/n$. $\square$

We have just seen that the n n-th roots of unity are $1, \beta, \beta^2, \ldots, \beta^{n-1}$, where $\beta = \cos(2\pi/n) + i\sin(2\pi/n)$. This is a special case of the following theorem.

THEOREM 11. *If z is a primitive n-th root of unity, then the n n-th roots of unity are $1, z, z^2, \ldots, z^{n-1}$.*

Proof. Since z is an n-th root, every integral power of z is also an n-th root, and so we need only show that the numbers

$$1, z, z^2, \ldots, z^{n-1}$$

are all different. If two of them, say, z^s and z^t, are the same and $s < t$, then $z^{t-s} = 1$, so that z is a $(t-s)$-th root. This is impossible, since z is a primitive n-th root and $t - s < n$. $\square$

THEOREM 12. *If z is a primitive n-th root of unity, then the primitive n-th roots of unity are the powers z^r of z such that r, n are relatively prime and $1 \leqslant r \leqslant n$.*

Proof. We have just seen that the n n-th roots are $z, z^2, z^3, \ldots, z^n$. Suppose that one of these, z^r, is a primitive n-th root, and let $c = (n, r)$. We must show that $c = 1$. Both n/c and r/c are positive integers, and

$$1 = (z^n)^{r/c} = (z^r)^{n/c},$$

so that z^r is an n/c-th root. Since z^r is a primitive n-th root, $n/c \geqslant n$, so that $c = 1$.

Now suppose that n, r are relatively prime and that $1 \leqslant r \leqslant n$. We have seen that z^r is an n-th root, and so in order to show that it is a primitive n-th root we need only suppose that it is an m-th root and then show that $m \geqslant n$. Since n, r are relatively prime, there are integers a, b such that $1 = na + rb$. If z^r is an m-th root, then

$$z^m = z^{m(na+rb)} = (z^n)^{am}(z^{rm})^b = 1,$$

so that z is an m-th root; and therefore, because z is a primitive n-th root, $m \geqslant n$ as required. $\square$

The above three theorems are entirely algebraic in nature, but we have appealed to our geometric intuition – in particular, to some properties of sine and cosine – in order to show that there are primitive n-th roots of unity for every positive integer n. The existence of these roots can be proved rigorously with the help of the fundamental theorem of algebra, or by developing the trigonometric functions analytically.

EXERCISES

1. Let z be a complex number such that $1, z, z^2, \ldots, z^{n-1}$ are the n n-th roots of unity, where $n > 1$. Show that z is a primitive n-th root of unity.

2. Show that a complex number z is a primitive n-th root of unity if and only if

$$(z^n - 1)/(z^s - 1) = 0$$

for all those positive integers s such that n/s is a prime integer.

Find the equation of least degree which is satisfied by all the primitive 24-th roots of unity.

3. Let a be a primitive m-th root of unity and let b be a primitive n-th root of unity. Show that ab is a primitive mn-th root of unity if and only if m and n are relatively prime.

Find all the primitive 12-th roots of unity in the form $u + iv$, where u, v are real numbers.

4. Solve the following equations:

(i) $z^2 = i$;

(ii) $z^3 = 1 + i\sqrt{3}$;

(iii) $(z+1)^4 + (z-1)^4 = 0$;

(iv) $(z+1)^6 = z^6$.

CHAPTER 3

SOME ALGEBRAIC STRUCTURES

1 Binary operations and groups

DEFINITION. A *binary operation* on a set G is a function from the set of ordered pairs of elements of G.

EXAMPLES. (i) The function defined by

$$f(\langle a, b \rangle) = a + b$$

for all real numbers a, b is a binary operation on **R**, because $a + b$ is uniquely determined by the ordered pair $\langle a, b \rangle$.
(ii) The function defined by

$$f(\langle a, b \rangle) = a + ib$$

for all real numbers a, b is a binary operation on **R**, because the complex number $a + ib$ is uniquely determined by $\langle a, b \rangle$.

Binary operations will be denoted by symbols such as $+$, $\cdot$, or $\oplus$, the image of the ordered pair $\langle a, b \rangle$ being denoted by $a + b$, $a \cdot b$, or $a \oplus b$ respectively. It is entirely a matter of convenience what particular symbol we use for a given operation as long as we are consistent, but if an operation is usually referred to as 'addition' then it will be denoted by $+$, rather than by $\cdot$ or $\oplus$, and $a + b$ will be called the 'sum' of a and b; and if the operation is usually referred to as 'multiplication' then it will be denoted by $\cdot$ and $a \cdot b$ will be called the 'product' of a and b.

If H is a subset of a set G and $\oplus$ is a binary operation on G, then the function defined by

$$f(\langle a, b \rangle) = a \oplus b$$

for all $a, b \in H$, is clearly a binary operation on H. It is called the *restriction* of $\oplus$ to H. We will denote it by $\oplus$, the same symbol that is used for the original binary operation. This will simplify the notation and should lead to no confusion provided it is remembered that, if $H \neq G$, then the operations '$\oplus$ on G' and '$\oplus$ on H' are not the same since they apply to different sets.

DEFINITIONS. A binary operation $\oplus$ on a set G is *closed*, or G is *closed with respect to* $\oplus$, if $a \oplus b \in G$ for all $a, b \in G$. A binary operation $\oplus$ on G is *associative* if $a \oplus (b \oplus c) = (a \oplus b) \oplus c$ for all $a, b, c \in G$.

We note that, if a binary operation is associative, then every restriction of it is also associative; but, as we see in the next example, a restriction of a closed operation need not be closed.

EXAMPLES. (i) The set **R** of real numbers is closed with respect to addition, since the sum of two real numbers is a real number. It was proved in Theorem 3(i), p. 44, that the addition of real numbers is associative. The restriction of addition to the set of all odd integers is not closed, since the sum of two odd integers is not odd.

(ii) The binary operation on **R** defined by

$$f(\langle a, b \rangle) = (a + b)/2$$

for all real numbers a, b, is clearly closed – the average of two real numbers is a real number. It is easily seen that this operation is not associative, and that its restriction to the set of integers is not closed.

If a set G is closed with respect to an operation $+$, then the *sum* $\sum_{i=1}^{n} a_i$ of a finite sequence $a_1, a_2, a_3, \ldots, a_n$ of elements from G is defined inductively by the conditions:

(i) $\sum_{i=1}^{1} a_i = a_1$;

(ii) $\sum_{i=1}^{n} a_i = \sum_{i=1}^{n-1} a_i + a_n$.

The proof that $\sum_{i=1}^{n} a_i$ is uniquely defined for all such finite sequences is similar to that of Theorem 10, p. 18; the closure of $+$ is used in showing that $\sum_{i=1}^{n} a_i$ is defined for $n > 2$. If the operation is denoted by $\cdot$ instead of by $+$, then $\sum_{i=1}^{n} a_i$ is usually denoted by $\prod_{i=1}^{n} a_i$, and referred to as the *product* of the finite sequence. If $+$ is closed and associative, then a general associative law holds:

$$\sum_{i=1}^{n} a_i = \sum_{i=1}^{s} a_i + \sum_{i=1}^{n-s} a_{s+i}$$

for every finite sequence $a_1, a_2, a_3, \ldots, a_n$ of elements from G and every integer s such that $1 \leqslant s < n$. The proof is similar to that of Theorem 11, p. 21.

DEFINITION. A *group* is a set G and a binary operation $\cdot$ on G with the properties:

(i) the operation $\cdot$ is closed;

(ii) the operation $\cdot$ is associative;

(iii) there is an element $I \in G$ such that $a \cdot I = I \cdot a = a$ for all $a \in G$; such an element is called an *identity* of the group;

(iv) for each element $a \in G$, there is an element $b \in G$ such that $a \cdot b = b \cdot a = I$; such an element b is called an *inverse* of a.

A group will be denoted by a symbol like $(G, \cdot)$, G being the set and $\cdot$ the binary operation on G. By the 'elements of the group $(G, \cdot)$' and the 'subsets of the group $(G, \cdot)$' we mean the elements and subsets of the set G; This misuse of the terms 'elements' and 'subsets' should not cause any confusion. A set G will be said to be a *group under the binary operation* $\cdot$ if $(G, \cdot)$ is a group, and $\cdot$ will be called the *group operation*. It should be noted that a set by itself is not a group; there must be an associated operation.

EXAMPLES. (i) We have already noted that the operation of addition on the set of real numbers is closed and associative. The number 0 is an identity, and an inverse of a real number a is $-a$. Thus the set of real numbers is a group under addition. Similarly, the set of integers, the set of rational numbers, the set of complex numbers, and the set of residue classes modulo a fixed integer are groups under addition.

(ii) The set of non-0 real numbers is easily seen to be a group under multiplication. The set of *all* real numbers is not a group under multiplication, since 0 does not have an inverse.

(iii) If n is a prime integer and $n \neq \pm 1$, then the set of non-[0] residue classes modulo n is a group under multiplication:

(a) If $[a]$ and $[b]$ are non-[0] residue classes modulo n, then n does not divide a and does not divide b. By Theorem 17(ii), p. 27, n does not divide ab, and so

$$[a][b] = [ab] \neq [0].$$

Thus, the set of non-[0] residue classes modulo n is closed with respect to multiplication.

(b) The associativity of multiplication was stated as Theorem 21(ii), p. 31.

(c) Since $n \neq \pm 1$, the residue class [1] is not [0]. By Theorem 21(vi), p. 31, it is the required identity.

(d) If A is a non-[0] residue class then, by Theorem 22(ii), p. 32, there is a residue class D such that $AD = DA = [1]$. Since $[1] \neq [0]$, D cannot be [0].

(iv) The set of integers is a group under the operation $\oplus$ defined by:

$$a \oplus b = \begin{cases} a + b & \text{if } a \text{ is even} \\ a - b & \text{if } a \text{ is odd} \end{cases}$$

This operation is obviously closed, and the proof of its associativity is tedious but straightforward. The integer 0 is an identity, and an inverse for a is $-a$ or a, according as a is even or odd. We note that the equality $a \oplus b = b \oplus a$ does not always hold. For example, $1 \oplus 2 = 1 - 2 = -1$ and $2 \oplus 1 = 2 + 1 = 3$.

DEFINITION. A group $(G, \cdot)$ is *commutative* (or *abelian*) if $a \cdot b = b \cdot a$ for all $a, b \in G$.

The only non-commutative group that we have encountered thus far is that given as Example (iv) above.

If $(G, \cdot)$ is a commutative group, then

$$\prod_{i=1}^{n} a_i = \prod_{i=1}^{n} a_{g(i)},$$

for any finite sequence $a_1, a_2, a_3, \ldots, a_n$ of elements from G and any bijection g from $]1, n[$ to $]1, n[$. This result is called the *general commutative law*. Its proof is similar to that of the general commutative law of the addition of integers, p. 22.

THEOREM 1. *A group $(G, \cdot)$ has only one identity, and each element of G has only one inverse. If the inverse of $a \in G$ is denoted by a', then $(a')' = a$ and $(a \cdot b)' = b' \cdot a'$ for all $a, b \in G$.*

Proof. Let I and e be identities of the group. Then $I = I \cdot e$ because e is an identity, and $e = I \cdot e$ because I is an identity. Therefore $I = e$.

Let $a \in G$, and suppose that a' and f are inverses for a. Then

$$a' = a' \cdot I = a' \cdot (a \cdot f) = (a' \cdot a) \cdot f = I \cdot f = f.$$

The element $(a')'$ is, by its definition, the solution to the equations

$$a' \cdot x = x \cdot a' = I.$$

Since a satisfies these equations, $a = (a')'$.

We have

$$\begin{aligned}
(a \cdot b) \cdot (b' \cdot a') &= a \cdot ((b \cdot b') \cdot a') \\
&= a \cdot a' \\
&= I,
\end{aligned}$$

and similarly

$$(b' \cdot a') \cdot a \cdot b = I.$$

Thus $(a \cdot b)' = b' \cdot a'$. $\square$

DEFINITION. Let $(G, \cdot)$ be a group, let $a \in G$, and let n be an integer. The *n-th power of a* is

(i) $\prod\limits_{i=1}^{n} a_i$, where $a_i = a$ for all i, if $n > 0$;

(ii) b^{-n}, where b is the inverse of a, if $n < 0$;

(iii) the identity of the group, if $n = 0$.

If a group operation is denoted by $\cdot$, as it was in the above definition, then the n-th power of an element a is denoted by a^n. In particular, the inverse of a is a^{-1}. If the operation is denoted by $+$, then the n-th power of a is denoted by na and the inverse of a, which is $(-1)a$, is denoted by $-a$. Also, the sum $b + (-a)$ is usually written as $b - a$.

Tʜᴇᴏʀᴇᴍ 2. *If $(G, \cdot)$ is a group, $a \in G$, and n, m are integers, then $(a^n)^m = a^{nm}$ and $a^n \cdot a^m = a^{n+m}$.*

The proof of this theorem consists of many separate cases, depending on whether n, m, nm, and $n + m$ are positive, negative, or 0; but it is not at all difficult, and it is left to the reader. The second part of the theorem explains our somewhat arbitrary definition of a^0. If $a^n \cdot a^m = a^{n+m}$ is to hold for all integers n, m, then, in particular, $a^{-1} \cdot a^1 = a^{-1+1} = a^0$, so that a^0 must be the identity of the group.

Dᴇꜰɪɴɪᴛɪᴏɴ. A group $(G, \cdot)$ is *cyclic* if there is an element $a \in G$ such that every element of G is a power of a. Such an element a is called a *generator* of the group.

Exᴀᴍᴘʟᴇs. (i) The set of integers under addition is a cyclic group. The group has two generators, 1 and -1.

(ii) It is easily verified by calculation that the set of non-[0] residue classes modulo 5 under multiplication is a cyclic group, with generators [2] and [3].

(iii) Let n be a positive integer. We show that the set of n-th roots of unity is a cyclic group under multiplication.
(a) If a and b are n-th roots of unity, then $(ab)^n = a^n b^n = 1$. Thus the product of two n-th roots of unity is an n-th root of unity.
(b) If a, b, c are n-th roots of unity, then $a(bc) = (ab)c$, since this holds for all complex numbers a, b, c.
(c) The number 1 is an n-th root of unity, and is an identity for the group.
(d) If a is an n-th root of unity, then $(1/a)^n = 1/a^n = 1$, so that $1/a$ is also an n-th root.
(e) By Theorem 11, p. 61, the group of n-th roots of unity is generated by any primitive n-th root.

If a group is cyclic, then it is necessarily commutative since $a^n \cdot a^m = a^{n+m} = a^{m+n} = a^m \cdot a^n$. Thus a non-commutative group cannot be cyclic. However, a commutative group need not be cyclic. For example, the set of rational numbers under addition is a commutative group; but it is not cyclic, because if a is a non-0 rational number, then $a/2$, for example, is not a 'power' (that is, an integral multiple) of a.

DEFINITION. The *order* of an element a of a group $(G, \cdot)$ is the smallest positive integer n such that a^n is the identity of the group. If there is no such integer, then the order of a is 0.

Clearly, every element in a group has a unique order. For example, in the group of non-[0] residue classes modulo 5 under multiplication, the orders of [1], [2], [3], [4] are 1, 4, 4, 2 respectively. This can be verified by finding the powers of the elements. As we shall see later, it is no coincidence that the generators of this group are those elements whose order is 4, the number of elements in the group, or that the orders all divide 4.

By the definition of the term 'primitive', an n-th root of unity is primitive if and only if it is an element of order n in the group of n-th roots of unity. In Theorem 10, p. 61, we proved that if z is a primitive n-th root and $z^m = 1$, then n divides m. This is a special case of the next result.

THEOREM 3. *If $(G, \cdot)$ is a group, $a \in G$ is of order n, and m is an integer such that a^m is the group identity, then $n \mid m$.*

Proof. Since $a^{|m|}$ is either a^m or $(a^m)^{-1}$, $a^{|m|}$ is the group identity. Therefore, if $m \neq 0$ there is a positive integer p such that a^p is the identity and so, by the well-ordering theorem for the positive integers, a has a non-0 order. Thus, if $n = 0$, then $m = 0$, so that $n \mid m$.

If $n \neq 0$, then the proof proceeds as it did for the n-th roots: we let q, r be integers such that $m = nq + r$ and $0 \leqslant r < n$, and we show that a^r is the identity and thus, using the definition of order, that $r = 0$. $\square$

EXERCISES

1. Determine in which of the following cases the binary operation $\oplus$ on the set of positive integers is associative, and also in which of them it is closed if restricted to the set of even integers:
(i) $a \oplus b = (a, b)$, the greatest common divisor of a and b;
(ii) $a \oplus b = a^b$;
(iii) $a \oplus b =$ the number of prime factors in ab;
(iv) $a \oplus b =$ the largest prime factor in ab.

2. Which of the following sets are groups under the indicated operations?
(i) the complex numbers with absolute value 1, under multiplication;
(ii) the even integers, under addition;
(iii) the odd integers, under addition;

(iv) those complex numbers which are roots of unity, under multiplication;
(v) the positive rational numbers, under the operation which associates a/b with the ordered pair $\langle a, b \rangle$.

3. Let G be the set of all subsets of a set X. Are $(G, \cup)$ and $(G, \cap)$ groups? If A, B are subsets of X, we denote the set of those elements which are in A and not in B by $A - B$ and define the operations $\oplus$ and $\otimes$ on G by

$$A \oplus B = (A - B) \cup (B - A)$$
and
$$A \otimes B = (A \cap B) \cup (X - (A \cup B)).$$

Show that $(G, \oplus)$ and $(G, \otimes)$ are commutative groups.

4. Show that, if the set of non-[0] residue classes modulo n is a group under multiplication, then n is prime and $n \neq \pm 1$.

5. Let $+$ be a closed and associative binary operation on a set G with the properties:
(i) there is an element $0 \in G$ such that $0 + a = a$ for all $a \in G$;
(ii) for every $a \in G$ there is an element $-a$ such that $-a + a = 0$.
Show that $(G, +)$ is a group.

6. Let $+$ be a closed and associative binary operation on a non-empty set G with the property: if a, $b \in G$, then there are elements c, $d \in G$ such that $a + c = b$ and $d + a = b$. Show that $(G, +)$ is a group.

7. Show that a group $(G, \cdot)$ is commutative if and only if $(a \cdot b)^2 = a^2 \cdot b^2$ for all a, $b \in G$.

8. Show that, if every element in a group is of order 1 or 2, then the group is commutative.

9. Show that, for every element a in a group, a and its inverse have the same order.

2 Subgroups

DEFINITION. A *subgroup* of a group $(G, \cdot)$ is a subset of G which is a group under the operation $\cdot$.

Here we are misusing the terms 'operation' and 'group' according to the conventions of the preceding section. To be precise, a subgroup of a group $(G, \cdot)$ is a group $(H, \odot)$ such that:
(i) H is a subset of G;
(ii) $a \cdot b = a \odot b$ for all a, $b \in H$.

EXAMPLES. (i) Every group has two trivial subgroups, the group itself and the set containing only the identity.

(ii) Under addition, the set of integers is a subgroup of the set of rational numbers, which is a subgroup of the set of real numbers, which is a subgroup of the set of complex numbers.

(iii) If a is an element of a group $(G, \cdot)$, then the set of all powers of a, that is,

$$\{a^0, a^1, a^{-1}, a^2, a^{-2}, \ldots\},$$

is clearly a cyclic subgroup of G. It is called the *subgroup generated by a*.

If $(H, \cdot)$ is a subgroup of a group $(G, \cdot)$, and I is the identity of G, then

$$a \cdot I = I \cdot a = a$$

for all $a \in H$, since these equations hold for all $a \in G$. Therefore I is the identity of $(H, \cdot)$. The inverse of $a \in H$ is that element $b \in H$ such that $a \cdot b = b \cdot a = I$. But there is only one element in G which satisfies these equations; it is the inverse of a relative to $(G, \cdot)$. Therefore the inverse of $a \in H$ is the inverse of a regarded as an element of the group $(G, \cdot)$.

THEOREM 4. *Let $(G, \cdot)$ be a group, and let H be a non-empty subset of G which is closed with respect to the operation $\cdot$. If either of the following two conditions holds, then $(H, \cdot)$ is a subgroup of $(G, \cdot)$:*
(i) *if $a \in H$, then $a^{-1} \in H$.*
(ii) *H contains just a finite number of elements.*

Proof. We need only show that $I \in H$ and that, if $a \in H$, then $a^{-1} \in H$.

First let us assume (i). Since H is non-empty, there is an element $b \in H$. By (i), $I = b \cdot b^{-1} \in H$.

Now suppose that H contains exactly n elements. Let $a \in H$. Since H is closed, the elements $a, a^2, a^3, \ldots, a^{n+1}$ are in H, and so two of them must be the same element. Suppose that $a^r = a^s$, where r, s are integers and $1 \leqslant r < s \leqslant n+1$. Since $(G, \cdot)$ is a group, $a^{s-r} = I$ and $a^{-1} = a^{s-r-1}$. But $a^m \in H$ for all positive integers m, and so $I \in H$. If $s - r - 1 = 0$, then $a^{-1} = I$, and so $a^{-1} \in H$; if $s - r - 1 > 0$, a^{-1} is a positive integral power of a and so is in H. $\square$

DEFINITIONS. The *order* of a group $(G, \cdot)$ is the number of elements in G if this is finite, and is 0 if G contains an infinite number of elements. If G contains just a finite number of elements, then $(G, \cdot)$ is a *finite* group.

THEOREM 5. *If an element a of a group $(G, \cdot)$ has order n, then the subgroup generated by a has order n.*

Proof. Suppose first that the order of a is 0. If there are integers r, s such that $a^r = a^s$ and $r < s$, then a^{s-r} is the group identity, and therefore a has non-0 order, contrary to hypothesis. Thus the elements $a^0, a^1, a^{-1}, a^2, a^{-2}, \ldots$ are all different, and so the subgroup generated by a has order 0.

Now suppose that a has non-0 order n. Consider the set $\{a^0, a^1, a^2, \ldots, a^{n-1}\}$. We show that every power of a is in this set, and that this set contains precisely n elements, thus completing the proof of the theorem.

(i) Let m be an integer. Since $n > 0$, there are integers q and r such that $m = nq + r$ and $0 \leqslant r < n$. By Theorem 2 and the fact that a^n is the group identity,

$$a^m = a^{nq+r} = (a^n)^q \cdot a^r = a^r.$$

Thus a^m is in the set $\{a^0, a^1, a^2, \ldots, a^{n-1}\}$.

(ii) If $a^r = a^s$, where $0 \leqslant r < s \leqslant n - 1$, then a^{s-r} is the group identity and $0 < s - r < n$, which contradicts the assumption that n is the order of a. □

EXAMPLE. Consider the group of 6-th roots of unity. If z is a primitive 6-th root, then it generates this group, the elements of the group being $1, z, z^2, z^3, z^4, z^5$. These elements have orders 1, 6, 3, 2, 3, 6 respectively, and so they generate subgroups of these orders. In fact, these are the only subgroups of this group for, as we shall now see, every subgroup of a cyclic group is generated by some element.

THEOREM 6. *Every subgroup of a cyclic group is cyclic.*

Proof. Let $(H, \cdot)$ be a subgroup of a cyclic group $(G, \cdot)$, and let a be a generator of G. Every element in G, and hence every element in H, is a power of a. Let n be an integer such that $a^n \in H$. If the only possible choice of n is $n = 0$, then H contains only the identity and thus is cyclic. Therefore we can assume that there is a non-0 integer n such that $a^n \in H$ and, since $a^{-n} = (a^n)^{-1}$, we can assume that $a^n \in H$ for some positive integer n. Let n be the smallest positive integer such that $a^n \in H$. We shall show that a^n generates H and thus prove the theorem.

Let $b \in H$. Then, since $b \in G$, there is an integer m such that $b = a^m$. By the division theorem, there are integers q and r such that $m = nq + r$ and $0 \leqslant r < n$. Since

$$a^r = a^{m-nq} = (a^m) \cdot (a^n)^{-q},$$

$a^m \in H$, $a^n \in H$, and H is a group, the element a^r is in H. But $0 \leqslant r < n$, and so, by the definition of n, $r = 0$. Therefore every element of H is a power of a^n. Also, every power of a^n is in H, since $a^n \in H$ and H is a group. Thus a^n is a generator of $(H, \cdot)$. □

EXAMPLE. Consider the group of all integers under addition. Here the n-th power of an integer a is na. The group is cyclic, with generators 1 and -1. If H is a subgroup, then, by the above theorem, H must be the set of all multiples of some integer.

EXERCISES

1. Let H and K be subgroups of a group G. Show that:
(i) $H \cap K$ is a subgroup of G;

(ii) $H \cup K$ is a subgroup of G if and only if $H \subseteq K$ or $K \subseteq H$.

2. Let G be a commutative group. Show that the following sets are subgroups of G:

(i) those elements of G whose order divides a fixed integer;

(ii) those elements of G whose order is non-0.

3. Give an example of a group with 0 order such that each of its elements has non-0 order.

4. Show that the set of all ordered pairs $\langle a, b \rangle$ of complex numbers a, b, where $b \neq 0$, is a non-commutative group under the binary operation $\cdot$ defined by

$$\langle a, b \rangle \cdot \langle c, d \rangle = \langle a + bc, bd \rangle.$$

Let n be a fixed positive integer.

(i) Find all the group elements P such that P^n is the group identity.

(ii) Show that the set of all elements of the form $\langle na - n, a \rangle$ is a commutative subgroup.

5. Find the orders of the elements of the group of residue classes modulo 12 under addition. Find all the subgroups of this group.

6. Show that the order of a subgroup of a cyclic group divides the order of the group. (In Theorem 17 we generalize this to any group.)

7. Let a be a generator of a cyclic group $(G, \cdot)$ of order $m \neq 0$ and let n be a positive integer. Show that a^n generates a subgroup of order $m/(n, m)$, and deduce that, if d is a positive integer which divides m, then there is one and only one subgroup of G of order d.

3   Groups of bijections

In this section we consider groups of bijections. The term 'bijection' was defined on p. 3.

DEFINITION. Let f and g be functions from a set A to A. The *composition*, $f \circ g$, of f and g is the function from A to A defined by

$$(f \circ g)(a) = f(g(a))$$

for all $a \in A$.

EXAMPLES. (i) Let f and g be the functions from **R**, the set of real numbers, to **R**, defined by

$$f(a) = a^2,$$
$$g(a) = a + 1,$$

for all $a \in$ **R**. Then,

$$(f \circ g)(a) = f(a+1) = (a+1)^2$$

and

$$(g \circ f)(a) = g(a^2) = a^2 + 1$$

for all $a \in$ **R**. We note that $f \circ g \neq g \circ f$.

6

(ii) Let A be any set which contains two different elements a, b, and let f be the function from A to A defined by

$$f(c) = a$$

for all $c \in A$. If g is a function from A to A, then $(g \circ f)(c) = g(a)$ and $(f \circ g)(c) = a$ for all $c \in A$. We note that there is no function g such that $(f \circ g)(b) = b$.

The operation of composition is obviously a closed binary operation on the set of all functions from a given set A to A. It is also associative: if f, g, h are functions from A to A and $a \in A$, then

$$(f \circ (g \circ h))(a) = f((g \circ h)(a))$$
$$= f(g(h(a)))$$

and
$$((f \circ g) \circ h)(a) = (f \circ g)(h(a))$$
$$= f(g(h(a))),$$

so that $f \circ (g \circ h) = (f \circ g) \circ h$. Furthermore, if i is the function defined by

$$i(a) = a$$

for all $a \in A$, then, clearly, $i \circ f = f \circ i = f$ for all functions f from A to A. Thus the set of all functions from A to A has three of the four group properties, under the operation of composition. However, a function need not have an inverse. In fact, if A contains two or more elements, then there are functions from A to A which do not have inverses, as we saw in Example (ii) above. Thus, if A contains two or more elements, then the set of all functions from A to A is not a group under composition.

THEOREM 7. *The set of all bijections from a set A to A is a group under the operation of composition.*

Proof. We must show that the four group properties hold.

(i) Let f and g be bijections from A to A. We must show that $f \circ g$ is a bijection from A to A. To show that it is a surjection, let $a \in A$ and let c be that element of A such that $f(c) = a$. There is such an element since f is a surjection and, since g is a surjection, there is an element $d \in A$ such that $g(d) = c$. We now have $a = (f \circ g)(d)$, and so $f \circ g$ is a surjection. To show that $f \circ g$ is an injection, suppose that $(f \circ g)(a) = (f \circ g)(b)$. Since f is an injection, $g(a) = g(b)$, and since g is an injection, $a = b$. Thus $f \circ g$ is an injection.

(ii) We have already noted that the operation of composition is associative.

(iii) The function i defined by $i(a) = a$ for all $a \in A$ is clearly a bijection and is the identity for the group.

(iv) Let f be a bijection. We must find a bijection g such that $(f \circ g)(a) = (g \circ f)(a) = a$ for all $a \in A$. The equation $(f \circ g)(a) = a$ suggests the definition of g. If $a \in A$ then, since f is a bijection, there is a unique element $b \in A$ such that $f(b) = a$. We define the function g by the condition: if $f(b) = a$, then $g(a) = b$. We have just seen that $g(a)$ is defined for all $a \in A$. Clearly, $(f \circ g)(a) = a$ for all $a \in A$. Also, if $a \in A$, then

$$f((g \circ f)(a)) = f(g(f(a))) = (f \circ g)(f(a)) = f(a)$$

and so, since f is an injection, $(g \circ f)(a) = a$. It only remains to show that g is a bijection: if $g(a) = g(b)$, then $(f \circ g)(a) = (f \circ g)(b)$, and so $a = b$; g is a surjection because $g(f(a)) = a$ for all $a \in A$. $\square$

Groups of bijections are studied in many branches of mathematics – for example, in geometry, in matrix theory, and in the reduction of quadratic forms – but we will confine ourselves here to the simplest possible case, the bijections from a finite set to itself.

DEFINITION. A *permutation* is a bijection from a finite set to itself. The *symmetric group on n symbols* is the group of bijections from the set $\{1, 2, 3, \ldots, n\}$ to this set. It is denoted by S_n.

In the above definition, we have only chosen the symbols $1, 2, 3, \ldots, n$ for convenience – S_n is the group of permutations of *any* set which contains exactly n elements, since these elements can be denoted by $1, 2, 3, \ldots, n$.

If $f \in S_n$, then $f(1), f(2), f(3), \ldots, f(n)$ are just the elements $1, 2, 3, \ldots, n$, possibly in a different order. Thus f can be thought of as a rearrangement of $1, 2, 3, \ldots, n$, or as the act of replacing 1 by $f(1)$, 2 by $f(2)$, and so on. We will denote f by

$$\begin{pmatrix} 1 & 2 & 3 & \ldots & n \\ f(1) & f(2) & f(3) & \ldots & f(n) \end{pmatrix}.$$

For example, if f is the permutation in S_3 defined by $f(1) = 2$, $f(2) = 3$, $f(3) = 1$, then f will be denoted by

$$\begin{pmatrix} 1 & 2 & 3 \\ 2 & 3 & 1 \end{pmatrix}.$$

Suppose that g is the permutation

$$\begin{pmatrix} 1 & 2 & 3 \\ 2 & 1 & 3 \end{pmatrix}.$$

Then

$$(f \circ g)(1) = f(g(1)) = f(2) = 3,$$

and similarly $(f \circ g)(2) = 2$ and $(f \circ g)(3) = 1$, so that

$$f \circ g = \begin{pmatrix} 1 & 2 & 3 \\ 3 & 2 & 1 \end{pmatrix}.$$

Similarly

$$g \circ f = \begin{pmatrix} 1 & 2 & 3 \\ 1 & 3 & 2 \end{pmatrix},$$

and we note that $f \circ g \neq g \circ f$, so that S_3 is a non-commutative group.

DEFINITIONS. An *s-cycle* or *cycle of length s* is a permutation $f \in S_n$ such that $f(a_1) = a_2$, $f(a_2) = a_3$, $f(a_3) = a_4, \ldots, f(a_s) = a_1$, for some subset $\{a_1, a_2, a_3, \ldots, a_s\}$ of s different elements from $\{1, 2, 3, \ldots, n\}$, and $f(a) = a$ for all other elements a of $\{1, 2, 3, \ldots, n\}$. Such a permutation will be denoted by $(a_1, a_2, a_3, \ldots, a_s)$ and will be said to *contain* the elements $a_1, a_2, a_3, \ldots, a_s$. Two cycles are *disjoint* if they do not contain any common element. A *transposition* is a 2-cycle.

EXAMPLES. (i) The permutation

$$\begin{pmatrix} 1 & 2 & 3 & 4 & 5 & 6 \\ 3 & 2 & 5 & 4 & 6 & 1 \end{pmatrix}$$

is a cycle in S_6, and can be denoted by $(1, 3, 5, 6)$, $(3, 5, 6, 1)$, $(5, 6, 1, 3)$ or $(6, 1, 3, 5)$. Note that it is *not* denoted by the bottom row $(3, 2, 5, 4, 6, 1)$ of the symbol for the permutation.

(ii) The identity permutation in S_n, that is, the permutation

$$\begin{pmatrix} 1 & 2 & 3 \ldots n \\ 1 & 2 & 3 \ldots n \end{pmatrix},$$

is a cycle which contains no elements. Here the usual notation for a cycle cannot be used and we will denote this identity by I_n.

We will now show that every permutation is a product of disjoint cycles. In order to make the proof clearer we first consider an example. Suppose that we wish to express

$$\begin{pmatrix} 1 & 2 & 3 & 4 & 5 & 6 \\ 3 & 1 & 2 & 6 & 5 & 4 \end{pmatrix}$$

as a product of disjoint cycles. First we choose any element in the permutation, say 3. Since 3 is replaced by 2, a cycle will begin $(3, 2, \ldots)$, and since 2 is replaced by 1, the cycle continues as $(3, 2, 1, \ldots)$, and since 1 is replaced by 3, the cycle is $(3, 2, 1)$. We now begin a new cycle by choosing another element, say 5. Since 5 is replaced by 5, the cycle containing 5 is just I_6 and we can ignore it. We now choose another element, say 4, and since this is replaced by 6, which is replaced by 4, the remaining cycle is $(4, 6)$. Thus the original permutation is

$$(3, 2, 1) \circ (4, 6).$$

THEOREM 8. *Every permutation is a product of disjoint cycles.*

Proof. We will prove the theorem by induction.

An element a is said to be *moved* by a permutation f if $f(a) \neq a$. If a permutation does not move any elements, then it is an identity and hence is a cycle. There are no permutations which move only one element, so the theorem holds trivially for such permutations.

Now let m be an integer, $m > 1$, and suppose that every permutation which moves less than m elements can be expressed as the product of disjoint cycles. Let f be a permutation in S_n which moves exactly m elements, and let a be an element which is moved by f. Consider the set $\{a, f(a), f^2(a), \ldots, f^n(a)\}$. This is a subset of $\{1, 2, 3, \ldots, n\}$, and so there must be integers s, t such that $s < t$ and $f^s(a) = f^t(a)$, from which $f^{t-s}(a) = a$. Thus $\{r \mid r$ is a positive integer and $f^r(a) = a\}$ is not empty, and so contains a smallest member k. It is easily seen that $(a, f(a), f^2(a), \ldots, f^{k-1}(a))$ is a cycle, which we denote by g.

Consider the permutation $h = f \circ g^{-1}$. It does not move any of $a, f(a), f^2(a), \ldots, f^{k-1}(a)$, and if b is not one of these elements, then $h(b) = f(b)$. Thus h moves less than m elements and therefore is a product of disjoint cycles. If an element is contained in one of these cycles, then it is moved by h, because these cycles are disjoint. Thus g is disjoint from each cycle in the factorization of h, and so we have expressed f, $= h \circ g$, as a product of disjoint cycles. □

THEOREM 9. *If $n \geqslant 2$, then every permutation in S_n is a product of transpositions.*

Proof. By the preceding theorem, we need only show that every cycle in S_n is a product of transpositions. A 0-cycle can be written $(1, 2) \circ (1, 2)$, and if $s \geqslant 1$, then an s-cycle $(a_1, a_2, a_3, \ldots, a_s)$ can be written as

$$(a_1, a_2, a_3, \ldots, a_s) = (a_1, a_s) \circ (a_1, a_{s-1}) \circ \ldots \circ (a_1, a_2),$$

the proof being by induction on s. □

For example, the permutation

$$\begin{pmatrix} 1 & 2 & 3 & 4 & 5 & 6 \\ 3 & 1 & 2 & 6 & 5 & 4 \end{pmatrix},$$

which we have already expressed as $(3, 2, 1) \circ (4, 6)$, can be written as $(3, 1) \circ (3, 2) \circ (4, 6)$. Also, we can insert terms like $(1, 2) \circ (1, 2)$ into this product without changing it, or we can express $(3, 1)$, for example, as $(2, 1) \circ (3, 2) \circ (2, 1)$, so the factorization of a permutation into transpositions is not unique. We now show that the parity (that is, the oddness or evenness) of the number of transpositions in a given product is uniquely determined by that product.

DEFINITIONS. A permutation is *even* if it is the product of an even number of transpositions and is *odd* if it is the product of an odd number of transpositions.

By the preceding theorem, if $n \geqslant 2$, then every permutation in S_n is even or odd. We now show that a permutation cannot be both even and odd. The proof of this is rather complicated[1]; the object of our proof is to obtain a function which associates an even integer with every even permutation and associates an odd integer with every odd permutation. The result then follows from the fact that no integer is both even and odd.

THEOREM 10. *A permutation cannot be both even and odd.*

Proof. We have seen that every permutation is a product of disjoint cycles. If $f \in S_n$ is so factorized as

$$f = c_1 \circ c_2 \circ c_3 \circ \ldots \circ c_r,$$

and a is moved by f, then a is contained in just one of the cycles c_1, c_2, $c_3, \ldots, c_r$, and hence must be followed in that cycle by $f(a)$. Therefore, those c_i that move at least one element are uniquely determined by f. We let $C(f)$ be the sum of the number of such cycles and the number of elements not moved by f. $C(f)$ is uniquely determined by f. For example, $C(I_n) = 0 + n = n$ and $C((1, 2)) = 1 + (n - 2) = n - 1$, where $(1, 2) \in S_n$.

Let (a, b) be a transposition in S_n. In computing $C(f \circ (a, b))$, three cases arise:

(i) a occurs in one of the cycles c_1, c_2, $c_3, \ldots, c_r$ and b occurs in another such cycle. Since the cycles are disjoint, their order in the product is immaterial, and we can suppose that a is contained in c_r and b is contained in c_{r-1}. Let $c_r = (a_1, a_2, a_3, \ldots, a_s, a)$ and $c_{r-1} = (b_1, b_2, b_3, \ldots, b_t, b)$. Then

$$c_{r-1} \circ c_r \circ (a, b) = (a_1, a_2, a_3, \ldots, a_s, a, b_1, b_2, b_3, \ldots, b_t, b),$$

so that the unique factorization of $f \circ (a, b)$ has one less term than the unique factorization of f, and $f \circ (a, b)$ and f move the same number of elements. Thus, in this case, $C(f \circ (a, b)) = C(f) - 1$.

(ii) a and b occur in the same cycle, which we can assume is c_r, and which must be of one of the following three types: (a, b), $(a, a_1, a_2, \ldots, a_s, b)$, $(a, a_1, a_2, \ldots, a_s, b, b_1, b_2, \ldots, b_t)$. If c_r is of the third type, then

$$c_r \circ (a, b) = (a_1, a_2, a_3, \ldots, a_s, b) \circ (b_1, b_2, b_3, \ldots, b_t, a),$$

so that $f \circ (a, b)$ contains one more factor than f and moves the same number of elements. Therefore, in this case, $C(f \circ (a, b)) = C(f) + 1$. The

---

[1] For another proof, see I. Halperin: Odd and even permutations, *Canadian Mathematical Bulletin* **3** (1960), 185.

other two cases are easier, with the same result, and are left to the reader.

(iii) At least one of a, b is not moved by f. In this case we have

$$C(f \circ (a, b)) = C(f) - 1.$$

Now let $t_1, t_2, t_3, \ldots, t_r$ be transpositions in S_n. By the preceding,

$$C(t_1) = n - 1,$$
$$C(t_1 \circ t_2) = n \text{ or } n - 2,$$
$$C(t_1 \circ t_2 \circ t_3) = n - 1 \text{ or } n - 3,$$

and, by an easy induction argument, we see that $n - C(t_1 \circ t_2 \circ t_3 \circ \ldots \circ t_r)$ is even if and only if r is even. Thus, $n - C(f)$ is even if f is an even permutation and is odd if f is an odd permutation. Since $n - C(f)$ is uniquely determined by f, and no integer is both even and odd, this proves the theorem. □

THEOREM 11. *If $n \geqslant 2$, then the set of all even permutations in S_n is a subgroup of S_n.*

Proof. The composition of two even permutations is even, since the sum of two even integers is even. We have already shown that composition is an associative operation. The identity is even since it can be expressed as $(1, 2) \circ (1, 2)$. If f is an even permutation and f^{-1} is odd, then $f \circ f^{-1}$ is also odd, since the sum of an even integer and an odd integer is odd; but $f \circ f^{-1}$ is the identity, which is even, and so f^{-1} must be even. □

DEFINITION. The set of all even permutations in S_n, where $n \geqslant 2$, is called the *alternating group on n symbols*, and is denoted by A_n.

Some subgroups of S_n can be found by considering the transformations of certain geometrical or physical objects onto themselves. For example, consider a square. By a *transformation of the square onto itself* we mean the result of a movement of the square which leaves it unchanged in position but, possibly, with its vertices permuted. The transformations can be physically realized by cutting a square out of paper and replacing it in all possible ways back in the hole.

Suppose that the vertices of the square are labelled 1, 2, 3, 4 clockwise around the square. A transformation of the square onto itself replaces 1 by, say, $f(1)$, 2 by $f(2)$, 3 by $f(3)$, and 4 by $f(4)$. The function f is obviously a permutation in S_4; we say that it is the permutation *associated with* the transformation. For example, suppose that the square is rotated clockwise by $\pi/2$. This transformation replaces 1 by 4, 2 by 1, 3 by 2, and 4 by 3, so the associated permutation is the cycle $(1, 4, 3, 2)$. It is easily seen, by considering the various possibilities, that there are eight possible transformations of the square onto itself, and they permute the vertices as follows: I_4, $(1, 4, 3, 2)$, $(1, 3) \circ (2, 4)$, $(1, 2, 3, 4)$, $(2, 4)$, $(1, 3)$, $(1, 2) \circ (3, 4)$, $(1, 4) \circ (2, 3)$.

The composition $f \circ g$ of two transformations f, g of the square onto itself is, by definition, the result of first performing the transformation g and then the transformation f. Clearly, $f \circ g$ can be found either by moving the square or by finding the composition of the associated permutations. For example, the composition of the transformations which permute the vertices first by $(1, 2, 3, 4)$ and then by $(1, 3)$ is the transformation which results in the permutation $(1, 3) \circ (1, 2, 3, 4) = (1, 2) \circ (3, 4)$, and this can also be found by first rotating the square clockwise by $3\pi/2$ and then reflecting the square in the 2, 4 diagonal. The result is a reflection in the 1, 4 side.

From the physical interpretation, the composition of two transformations of the square onto itself is again such a transformation and so, by Theorem 4, the set of associated permutations is a subgroup of S_4. It is called the 'group of the square'.

Each of the five regular polyhedra gives rise to a group of permutations, and the resulting groups and their various subgroups include many of the best known groups of low order.

EXERCISES

1. Show that a function f from a set A to A is:

(i) an injection if and only if there is a function g from A to A such that $(g \circ f)(a) = a$ for all $a \in A$;

(ii) a surjection if and only if there is a function g from A to A such that $(f \circ g)(a) = a$ for all $a \in A$.

2. Show that S_n is commutative if and only if $n = 1$ or 2.

3. Show that the inverse of the cycle $(a_1, a_2, a_3, \ldots, a_r)$ is the cycle $(a_r, a_{r-1}, a_{r-2}, \ldots, a_1)$, and deduce that the inverse of the permutation $f_1 \circ f_2 \circ f_3 \circ \ldots \circ f_s$, where the f_i are cycles, is $f'_s \circ f'_{s-1} \circ f'_{s-2} \circ \ldots \circ f'_1$, where f'_i is the cycle obtained by reversing the order of the elements in f_i.

4. Show that an s-cycle is even if and only if s is odd. Show that the composition of two transpositions in S_n, where $n \geqslant 3$, is either a 3-cycle or the composition of two 3-cycles. Deduce that a permutation in S_n, where $n \geqslant 3$, is even if and only if it is a composition of 3-cycles.

5. Show that the order of S_n is $n!$, and that, if $n \geqslant 2$, then the function F defined by

$$F(f) = f \circ (1, 2)$$

is a bijection from A_n to the set of all odd permutations in S_n. Deduce that the order of A_n is $n!/2$.

6. Determine whether the following permutations are even or odd, and express them in the two-rowed notation:

(i) $(2, 3, 5, 1) \circ (4, 3, 2, 1, 5)$;
(ii) $(2, 3, 1) \circ (2, 4, 3) \circ (3, 1, 4)$;
(iii) $(1, 4, 5, 3, 2) \circ (2, 3, 4)$.

7. Find subgroups of S_3 by considering the transformations of a triangle onto itself, and find a subgroup of S_4 by considering the transformations of a non-square rectangle onto itself.

8. Show that the order of a permutation is the least common multiple of the lengths of the disjoint cycles in its factorization, provided that the permutation is not an identity.

4 Isomorphisms and homomorphisms

DEFINITIONS. Let $(G, +)$ and $(H, \oplus)$ be groups. A *homomorphism from $(G, +)$ to $(H, \oplus)$* is a function f from G to H such that

$$f(a + b) = f(a) \oplus f(b)$$

for all $a, b \in G$. An *isomorphism from $(G, +)$ to $(H, \oplus)$* is a bijective homomorphism from $(G, +)$ to $(H, \oplus)$. If f is a homomorphism from $(G, +)$ to a group, then $f(G)$ is a *homomorphic image* of $(G, +)$.

EXAMPLES. (i) In Chapters 1 and 2 we saw that the functions defined as follows were injective homomorphisms:

(a) $f(a) = [\langle 1, 1 + a \rangle]$, from $\mathbf{Z}^+$ to $\mathbf{Z}$ (p. 12);
(b) $f(a) = a/1$, from $\mathbf{Z}$ to $\mathbf{Q}$ (p. 38);
(c) $f(a) = [(a)_i]$, from $\mathbf{Q}$ to $\mathbf{R}$ (p. 46);
(d) $f(a) = \langle a, 0 \rangle$, from $\mathbf{R}$ to $\mathbf{C}$ (p. 55).

In each case, the group operation was addition.

(ii) Let $(G, \cdot)$ and $(H, \odot)$ be cyclic groups of the same order n, with generators a, b respectively. We show that the function f defined by

$$f(a^m) = b^m$$

for all integers m, is an isomorphism from $(G, \cdot)$ to $(H, \odot)$. In the first place, it is a function: every element in G is a power of a, and so $f(c)$ is defined for all $c \in G$; if m and s are integers such that $a^m = a^s$ then, by Theorem 3, $n \mid (m - s)$ and so $b^m = b^s$. Therefore $f(c)$ is uniquely defined for all $c \in G$, and so f is a function. Every element in H is a power of b, and so f is a surjection. If $b^m = b^s$, then $n \mid (m - s)$ by Theorem 3, and thus $a^m = a^s$. Therefore f is an injection. Finally,

$$f(a^m \cdot a^s) = f(a^{m+s})$$
$$= b^{m+s}$$

$$f(a^m \cdot a^s) = b^m \odot b^s$$
$$= f(a^m) \odot f(a^s)$$

for all integers m, s.

(iii) It is easy to see that the function F defined by

$$F(f) = \begin{cases} [0] & \text{if } f \text{ is even} \\ [1] & \text{if } f \text{ is odd} \end{cases}$$

is a homomorphism from S_n to the group of residue classes modulo 2 under addition.

(iv) In §7 of this chapter we will show that the logarithmic functions exist, and that they are isomorphisms from the group of positive real numbers under multiplication to the group of all real numbers under addition. There is no isomorphism from the group of all non-0 real numbers under multiplication to the group of all real numbers under addition. For suppose that f is such a function. Then we would have

$$f(1) + f(1) = f(1 \cdot 1) = f(1),$$

so that $f(1) = 0$, and

$$f(-1) + f(-1) = f(-1 \cdot -1) = f(1) = 0,$$

so that $f(-1) = 0$. Thus f is not an injection, and hence is not an isomorphism.

The injective homomorphisms of Example (i) above were considered in some detail in Chapters 1 and 2, where they were used to embed one set in another. Generalizing the remarks made on pp. 12–13, (but ignoring the second operation, multiplication, for the moment) we see that if there is an injective homomorphism from a group $(G, +)$ to a group $(H, \oplus)$, then $(G, +)$ and $(f(G), \oplus)$ have precisely the same group structure. In particular, if f is an isomorphism, so that $f(G) = H$, then $(G, +)$ and $(H, \oplus)$ can be regarded as being essentially the same group. This suggests that the property of 'being isomorphic' is an equivalence relation, as we now prove.

THEOREM 12. *The relation defined by 'there is an isomorphism from $(G, +)$ to $(H, \oplus)$' is an equivalence relation.*

Proof. We must show that the three properties which characterize an equivalence relation hold.

(i) The function f defined by $f(a) = a$ for all elements a of a group $(G, +)$ is obviously an isomorphism from $(G, +)$ to $(G, +)$.

(ii) Suppose that f is an isomorphism from $(G, +)$ to $(H, \oplus)$. Since f

is a bijection it has an inverse, which is easily seen to be an isomorphism from $(H, \oplus)$ to $(G, +)$.

(iii) Let f be an isomorphism from $(G, +)$ to $(H, \oplus)$, and let g be an isomorphism from $(H, \oplus)$ to $(K, \cdot)$. The composition $g \circ f$ is, by Theorem 7, a bijection from G to K. If $a, b \in G$, then

$$
\begin{aligned}
(g \circ f)(a + b) &= g(f(a + b)) \\
&= g(f(a) \oplus f(b)) \\
&= g(f(a)) \cdot g(f(b)) \\
&= (g \circ f)(a) \cdot (g \circ f)(b).
\end{aligned}
$$

Thus, $g \circ f$ is an isomorphism. $\square$

Two groups will be said to be *isomorphic* if there is an isomorphism from one to the other. By (ii) in the above proof, such a form of expression will not lead to any confusion: if $(G, +)$ and $(H, \oplus)$ are isomorphic, then this can be taken to mean either that there is an isomorphism from G to H or that there is an isomorphism from H to G. However, the relation of being homomorphic is not symmetric – see Example (iii) above – and so two groups will never be said to be homomorphic.

THEOREM 13. *If f is a homomorphism from a group $(G, +)$ to a group $(H, \cdot)$, then:*
(i) $f(0) = I$, *where 0, I are the identities in G, H, respectively;*
(ii) $f(-a) = (f(a))^{-1}$ *for all $a \in G$, where $-a$ is the inverse of a and $(f(a))^{-1}$ is the inverse of $f(a)$;*
(iii) $f(G)$ *is a subgroup of H;*
(iv) *if f is an injection, then it is an isomorphism from $(G, +)$ to $(f(G), \cdot)$.*

Proof. (i) $f(0) = f(0 + 0) = f(0) \cdot f(0)$, from which $f(0) = I$;
(ii) $f(a) \cdot f(-a) = f(a - a) = f(0) = I$, and so $f(-a)$ is the inverse of $f(a)$;
(iii) If c, $d \in f(G)$, then there are elements a, $b \in G$ such that $c = f(a)$ and $d = f(b)$, so that

$$
c \cdot d = f(a) \cdot f(b) = f(a + b),
$$

and therefore $c \cdot d \in f(G)$. Thus $f(G)$ is closed with respect to the operation $\cdot$. Also $f(G)$ is not empty, by (i), and if $c \in f(G)$, then $c^{-1} \in f(G)$, by (ii). Therefore $f(G)$ is a subgroup of H, by Theorem 4(i);

(iv) This follows immediately from (iii) and the definition of the term 'isomorphism'. $\square$

It has already been pointed out that if two groups are isomorphic then they are, from a group-theoretic point of view, identical. The next theorem shows that group theory is just the study of groups of bijections. This result, limited to finite groups, has been variously attributed to Jordan, Cayley and Dyck.

THEOREM 14. *Every group is isomorphic to a group of bijections.*

Proof. Let $(G, \cdot)$ be a group and let $(B, \circ)$ be the group of bijections from G to G. We will show that $(G, \cdot)$ is isomorphic to a subgroup of $(B, \circ)$.

For each $g \in G$, let $F(g)$ be the function from G to G defined by

$$F(g)(a) = g \cdot a$$

for all $a \in G$. It is clear that F is a function from G to the set of all functions from G to G. We will show that it is an isomorphism from $(G, \cdot)$ to a subgroup of $(B, \circ)$. First we show that F is a function from G to B.

(i) Let $g, a, b \in G$, and suppose that $F(g)(a) = F(g)(b)$. Then $g \cdot a = g \cdot b$, and so $a = b$. Therefore $F(g)$ is an injection.

(ii) If $g, a \in G$, then $F(g)(g^{-1} \cdot a) = a$ and so $F(g)$ is a surjection. $F(g)$ is therefore a bijection, for all $g \in G$, and so F is a function from G to B.

To show that F is an injection, suppose that $F(a) = F(b)$. Then $a \cdot c = b \cdot c$ for all $c \in G$. In particular, $a \cdot I = b \cdot I$, and so $a = b$.

If $a, b, c \in G$, then

$$
\begin{aligned}
(F(a) \circ F(b))(c) &= F(a)(F(b)(c)) \\
&= F(a)(b \cdot c) \\
&= a \cdot (b \cdot c) \\
&= (a \cdot b) \cdot c \\
&= F(a \cdot b)(c).
\end{aligned}
$$

Thus $F(a) \circ F(b) = F(a \cdot b)$, and therefore F is a homomorphism.

The proof now follows from Theorem 13(iv). □

EXAMPLES. (i) Let G be the set $\{1, 2, 3, 4\}$, and define the operation $\odot$ on G by the table

$\odot$	1	2	3	4
1	1	2	3	4
2	2	1	4	3
3	3	4	1	2
4	4	3	2	1 .

If $a, b \in G$, then $a \odot b$ is defined to be that element which is found at the intersection of the row beginning with a and the column beginning with b. This operation is closed since every element in the body of the table is in

G. The proof of its associativity requires a considerable amount of calculation and is left for the reader. For example, $2 \odot (4 \odot 3) = 2 \odot 2 = 1$ and $(2 \odot 4) \odot 3 = 3 \odot 3 = 1$, so that $2 \odot (4 \odot 3) = (2 \odot 4) \odot 3$. The element 1 is obviously an identity, and the inverses of 1, 2, 3, 4 are 1, 2, 3, 4 respectively. Thus $(G, \odot)$ is a group. It is called the *Klein 4-group*. By Theorem 14, it is isomorphic to a group of bijections from $\{1, 2, 3, 4\}$ to $\{1, 2, 3, 4\}$, that is, it is isomorphic to a subgroup of S_4. The proof of the theorem shows how a suitable isomorphism F can be defined. $F(2)$, for example, is the permutation such that

$$F(2)(1) = 2 \odot 1 = 2,$$
$$F(2)(2) = 2 \odot 2 = 1,$$
$$F(2)(3) = 2 \odot 3 = 4,$$
$$F(2)(4) = 2 \odot 4 = 3,$$

so that $F(2)$ is $(1, 2) \circ (3, 4)$.

(ii) Consider the group $(\mathbf{R}, +)$ of all real numbers under addition. This group is isomorphic to a subgroup of the group of bijections from $\mathbf{R}$ to $\mathbf{R}$, and a suitable isomorphism F associates with $g \in \mathbf{R}$ the bijection $F(g)$ defined by

$$F(g)(a) = g + a.$$

EXERCISES

1. Find homomorphisms from the group of residue classes modulo 8 to:
(i) the group of residue classes modulo 4;
(ii) the group of residue classes modulo 2.

2. Show that the function f defined by
$$f(a) = a^{-1},$$
for all $a \in G$, is an isomorphism from a group $(G, \cdot)$ to $(G, \cdot)$ if and only if $(G, \cdot)$ is commutative.

3. Let G and H be cyclic groups, of order n and m respectively. Show that there is a surjective homomorphism from G to H if and only if $m \mid n$.

4. Let f be a homomorphism from a group G to G. Show that $\{g \mid g \in G$ and $f(g) = g\}$ is a subgroup of G.

5. Using the method employed in the proof of Theorem 14, find groups of bijections which are isomorphic to each of the following groups:
(i) the non-0 real numbers under multiplication;
(ii) S_3;
(iii) the non-[0] residue classes modulo 5 under multiplication.

6. Show that a cyclic group G has order 0 if and only if it contains a subgroup different from G but isomorphic to G.

7. Show that the group of rational numbers under addition is not isomorphic to the group of positive rational numbers under multiplication.

5   Factor groups

In this section we will show how all the homomorphisms from a given group $(G, \cdot)$ can be found by considering the subgroups of G. First we show that every homomorphic image of G is isomorphic to a group $(F, \times)$ whose elements are subsets of G, then that any one of these subsets completely determines the homomorphism, and finally that one of these subsets is a subgroup of G.

Let f be a homomorphism from $(G, \cdot)$ to a group $(H, \odot)$. For each $a \in G$, let $[a] = \{b \,|\, b \in G \text{ and } f(a) = f(b)\}$, and let F be the set of all these subsets $[a]$ of G. The function h defined by

$$h([a]) = f(a),$$

for all $[a] \in F$, is clearly a bijection from F to $f(G)$: it is an injection, by the definition of F, and a surjection, by the definition of $f(G)$. We have already shown in Theorem 13(iii) that $f(G)$ is a subgroup of H, and so, if we define the product $[a] \times [b]$ of $[a], [b] \in F$ to be that set $[c] \in F$ such that

$$h([c]) = h([a]) \odot h([b]),$$

then $(F, \times)$ is clearly a group and h is an isomorphism from $(F, \times)$ to $(f(G), \odot)$. For all we have done, in effect, is to apply the operation $\odot$, not to the elements of $f(G)$, but to the corresponding elements of F. We have now shown that every homomorphic image of G is isomorphic to a group whose elements are subsets of G.

If $a, b \in G$, then

$$\begin{aligned} f(a \cdot b) &= f(a) \odot f(b) \\ &= h([a]) \odot h([b]), \end{aligned}$$

since f is a homomorphism. Thus, by the definition of the operation $\times$,

$$[a] \times [b] = [a \cdot b].$$

Therefore, if the elements of F are given, then the operation $\times$ can be defined without any reference to the original homomorphism f. Now suppose that $[a] \in F$ and that $b \in G$. Then $c \in [b]$ if and only if $f(c^{-1} \cdot b \cdot a) = f(a)$, that is, if and only if $c^{-1} \cdot b \cdot a \in [a]$. Therefore, if one element of F is known, then all the elements of F can be found; and, by the preceding remark, the group $(F, \times)$ is then completely determined. Also, the function k defined by

$$k(a) = [a]$$

for all $a \in G$ is a homomorphism from $(G, \cdot)$ to $(F, \times)$, because $k(a \cdot b) =$ $[a \cdot b] = [a] \times [b]$. Now recall that the isomorphism h effectively replaces $[a]$ by $f(a)$. If $[a]$ is replaced by $f(a)$ in the definition of k, then we have $k(a) = f(a)$. That is, k is the original homomorphism f. Thus we have the result: if isomorphic groups are regarded as identical, then the original homomorphism f can be completely reconstructed from one element of F.

In particular, f can be found if that element of F which contains the identity of G is given. By Theorem 13(i), this element is $\{a \mid a \in G$ and $f(a)$ is the identity of $H\}$. We now show that this element is a subgroup of G.

DEFINITION. The *kernel* of a homomorphism f from a group $(G, \cdot)$ to a group $(H, \odot)$ is the set $\{a \mid a \in G$ and $f(a)$ is the identity of $H\}$.

THEOREM 15. *If K is the kernel of a homomorphism f from a group $(G, \cdot)$ to a group $(H, \odot)$, then*:
(i) $(K, \cdot)$ *is a subgroup of* $(G, \cdot)$;
(ii) $a^{-1} \cdot b \cdot a \in K$ *for all $a \in G$ and all $b \in K$.*

Proof. (i) Let $a, b \in K$, and let I be the identity of H. Then

$$f(a \cdot b) = f(a) \odot f(b) = I \odot I = I,$$

and, by Theorem 13(ii),

$$f(a^{-1}) = (f(a))^{-1} = I^{-1} = I.$$

By Theorem 13(i), K is not empty, and so, by Theorem 4, $(K, \cdot)$ is a subgroup of $(G, \cdot)$.

(ii) If $a \in G$ and $b \in K$, then

$$f(a^{-1} \cdot b \cdot a) = (f(a))^{-1} \odot f(b) \odot f(a)$$
$$= (f(a))^{-1} \odot f(a) = I. \ \square$$

DEFINITION. A subgroup $(L, \cdot)$ of a group $(G, \cdot)$ is *normal* if $a^{-1} \cdot b \cdot a \in L$ for all $a \in G$ and all $b \in L$.

We have just shown that the kernel of a homomorphism is a normal subgroup. Now we prove the converse.

THEOREM 16. *If $(K, \cdot)$ is a normal subgroup of a group $(G, \cdot)$, then there is a homomorphism from $(G, \cdot)$ for which K is the kernel.*

Proof. We are guided in this proof by knowing, from the first remarks in this section, precisely what the homomorphism must be.

For each $a \in G$, let $[a] = \{b \mid b \in G$ and $b \cdot a^{-1} \in K\}$. Let F be the set of all these subsets of G, and define the binary operation $\times$ on F by

$$[a] \times [b] = [a \cdot b].$$

We will show that $(F, \times)$ is a group which is a homomorphic image of $(G, \cdot)$, the homomorphism having kernel K. The first part of the proof – and the most difficult – consists of showing that $\times$ is actually a binary operation on F, that is, that $[a] \times [b]$ is uniquely determined by the ordered pair $\langle [a], [b] \rangle$.

Suppose that $a, a', b, b' \in G$ and that $[a] = [a']$ and $[b] = [b']$. Then, since K contains the identity, $a \in [a']$ and $b \in [b']$, and so there are elements $c, d \in K$ such that $a = c \cdot a'$ and $b = d \cdot b'$. We must show that $[a \cdot b]$ and $[a' \cdot b']$ are the same set, so suppose that $e \in [a \cdot b]$. Then $e = k \cdot a \cdot b$ for some $k \in K$, and thus

$$e = k \cdot c \cdot a' \cdot d \cdot b' = (k \cdot c \cdot a' \cdot d \cdot a'^{-1}) \cdot a' \cdot b'.$$

Since K is a subgroup, $k \cdot c \in K$, and since K is normal, $a' \cdot d \cdot a'^{-1} \in K$. Thus $e \in [a' \cdot b']$, and therefore $[a \cdot b] \subseteq [a' \cdot b']$. If a is interchanged with a' and b with b' in the above argument, then we obtain $[a' \cdot b'] \subseteq [a \cdot b]$; and so $[a' \cdot b'] = [a \cdot b]$, as required.

The associativity of $\times$ follows easily from the associativity of the operation $\cdot$ and is left to the reader. The element $[I]$, which is K, is obviously an identity, and an inverse for $[a] \in F$ is $[a^{-1}]$. Thus $(F, \times)$ is a group.

Now let f be the function defined by

$$f(a) = [a]$$

for all $a \in G$. It is a homomorphism from $(G, \cdot)$ to $(F, \times)$ since

$$f(a \cdot b) = [a \cdot b] = [a] \times [b] = f(a) \times f(b)$$

for all $a, b \in G$. The kernel of f is $\{a \mid [a] = [I]\} = K$. Note that f is a surjection. □

DEFINITIONS. Let $(K, \cdot)$ be a normal subgroup of a group $(G, \cdot)$. Let F be the set of all subsets of G of the type

$$[a] = \{b \mid b \in G \text{ and } b \cdot a^{-1} \in K\},$$

where a ranges over all the elements in G, and let $\times$ be the binary operation defined on F by

$$[a] \times [b] = [a \cdot b].$$

The group $(F, \times)$ is the *factor group* or *quotient group of* $(G, \cdot)$ *by* $(K, \cdot)$ and is denoted by $(G/K, \times)$; or, if the group operation on G is denoted by an addition symbol like $+$, then it is called the *difference group of* $(G, +)$ *by* $(K, +)$ and is denoted by $(G - K, \times)$. The function f from G to G/K defined by

$$f(a) = [a]$$

is the *canonical homomorphism from* $(G, \cdot)$ *induced by* K.

In Theorem 16 we proved that the factor group $(G/K, \times)$ is a group, and that the canonical homomorphism from $(G, \cdot)$ induced by K is a surjective homomorphism from $(G, \cdot)$ to $(G/K, \times)$ with kernel K.

By Theorems 15 and 16, a subset of a group is a kernel if and only if it is a normal subgroup. Thus we have now shown that all the homomorphisms from a group can be found if all its normal subgroups are known: with each normal subgroup there is associated a homomorphism for which this subgroup is the kernel, and if isomorphic groups are regarded as identical, then this homomorphism is uniquely determined by its kernel and can be completely described in terms of it.

EXAMPLE. Consider $(\mathbf{Z}, +)$, the group of all integers under addition. Every subgroup of $(\mathbf{Z}, +)$ is normal since $(\mathbf{Z}, +)$ is commutative, and is cyclic since $(\mathbf{Z}, +)$ is cyclic. Let $(K, +)$ be a subgroup with generator n. Then K is the set of all integral multiples of n, that is, K is the residue class $[0]$ modulo n. The element $[a] \in \mathbf{Z} - K$ is $\{b \,|\, b - a \in K\} = \{b \,|\, n$ divides $b - a\}$, and so $[a]$ is the residue class containing a modulo n. The operation $\times$ on $\mathbf{Z} - K$ is given by

$$[a] \times [b] = [a + b].$$

Thus, $(\mathbf{Z} - K, \times)$ is the group of residue classes modulo n, under the operation of addition that was defined on p. 30.

We have already seen that a homomorphic image of a group $(G, \cdot)$ is isomorphic to a factor group $(G/K, \times)$. The elements of G/K are subsets of G, two elements $a, b \in G$ being in the same element of G/K if and only if they have the same image under the homomorphism. In effect, the homomorphism has replaced a subset of G by a single element of G/K. Thus, in some intuitive sense, the set G/K is simpler, or no more complicated, than G. This suggests the use of homomorphisms in group theory: the study of a particular property of a group can sometimes be simplified if a suitable homomorphic image is studied instead of the original group. This is illustrated in some of the examples and exercises that follow.

DEFINITIONS. Let $(G, \cdot)$ be a group, and let H and K be subsets of G. The *product* $H \cdot K$ of H and K is the set $\{b \,|\, b = h \cdot k$ where $h \in H$ and $k \in K\}$. If the group operation on G is denoted by an addition symbol, then the product of H and K is referred to as the *sum* of H and K. If H contains just one element, h, then $H \cdot K$ and $K \cdot H$ are denoted by $h \cdot K$ and $K \cdot h$ and referred to as *left* and *right cosets* of K respectively.

If $[a]$ is an element of a factor group G/K, then
$$\begin{aligned} [a] &= \{c \,|\, c \in G \text{ and } c \cdot a^{-1} \in K\} \\ &= \{d \,|\, d = k \cdot a \text{ where } k \in K\} \\ &= K \cdot a. \end{aligned}$$

7

Thus G/K is the set of all right cosets of K. The product $(K \cdot a) \cdot (K \cdot b)$ is, by the above definition,

$$\{c \,|\, c = k \cdot a \cdot l \cdot b \text{ where } k, l \in K\}$$
$$= \{c \,|\, c = k \cdot (a \cdot l \cdot a^{-1}) \cdot a \cdot b \text{ where } k, l \in K\}$$
$$= \{c \,|\, c = m \cdot a \cdot b \text{ where } m \in K\}$$
$$= K \cdot (a \cdot b).$$

(An element of the form $k \cdot (a \cdot l \cdot a^{-1})$, where $k, l \in K$, is in K because K is normal, and hence $a \cdot l \cdot a^{-1} \in K$. An element $m \in K$ is of the form $k \cdot (a \cdot l \cdot a^{-1})$, where $k, l \in K$, since $m = m \cdot a \cdot I \cdot a^{-1}$.) The product of $K \cdot a = [a]$ and $K \cdot b = [b]$, regarded as elements of G/K, is

$$[a] \times [b] = [a \cdot b] = K \cdot (a \cdot b).$$

Thus, a factor group $(G/K, \times)$ is just the group of right cosets of K under the operation defined above.

EXAMPLES. (i) We noted that the only difficult part of the proof of Theorem 16 consisted in showing that the product of an ordered pair of elements from a factor group is uniquely defined by that ordered pair. When we defined the operations of addition on $\mathbf{R}$ and on the set of residue classes modulo n, the same difficulty arose. This was because these groups were constructed as difference groups. We have already shown, in the preceding example, that the group of residue classes is a difference group. To see that $(\mathbf{R}, +)$ was constructed as a difference group, let G be the set of all Cauchy sequences of rational numbers, and define the sum of two such sequences $(a_i)_i$, $(b_i)_i$ to be

$$(a_i)_i + (b_i)_i = (a_i + b_i)_i.$$

It is easily seen that $(G, +)$ is a commutative group. Let K be the set of those sequences that have the limit 0. Then K is a normal subgroup of G, and it should be apparent from the way in which the real numbers were defined that $G - K$ is the group $(\mathbf{R}, +)$.

(ii) Consider the set $\mathbf{Z}^+$ as a subset of the group $(\mathbf{Z}, +)$. A right coset $\mathbf{Z}^+ + a$ is

$$\mathbf{Z}^+ + a = \{c \,|\, c = n + a \text{ where } n \in \mathbf{Z}^+\}$$
$$= \{c \,|\, c > a\}$$

and the sum $(\mathbf{Z}^+ + a) + (\mathbf{Z}^+ + b)$ is

$$(\mathbf{Z}^+ + a) + (\mathbf{Z}^+ + b) = \{c \,|\, c = n + a + m + b \text{ where } n, m \in \mathbf{Z}^+\}$$
$$= \{c \,|\, c > a + b + 1\}$$
$$= \mathbf{Z}^+ + (a + b + 1).$$

The set of right cosets of $\mathbf{Z}^+$ is clearly a group under this operation, but it is not a difference group of $\mathbf{Z}$ by a normal subgroup of $\mathbf{Z}$ since none of the right cosets is a subgroup of $\mathbf{Z}$.

(iii) Let $K = \{0,1\}$ be considered as a subset of $(\mathbf{Z}, +)$. For each $a \in \mathbf{Z}$,

$$K + a = \{a, a+1\}.$$

The sum of two right cosets of K is not a right coset of K since it contains three integers.

The second part of the next theorem is usually attributed to Lagrange.

THEOREM 17. *Let $(S, \cdot)$ be a subgroup of a group $(G, \cdot)$. Then:*
(i) *each element of G is in exactly one left coset of S and in exactly one right coset of S;*
(ii) *if S contains exactly n elements and G contains exactly m elements, then $n \mid m$, and there are exactly m/n left and m/n right cosets of S.*

Proof. Consider the relation α defined on G by '$a \, \alpha \, b$ if and only if $a^{-1} \cdot b \in S$'. This is an equivalence relation:
(i) $a \, \alpha \, a$ for all $a \in G$, since $a^{-1} \cdot a = I \in S$;
(ii) if $a^{-1} \cdot b \in S$, then $(a^{-1} \cdot b)^{-1} = b^{-1} \cdot a \in S$;
(iii) if $a^{-1} \cdot b \in S$ and $b^{-1} \cdot c \in S$, then $a^{-1} \cdot b \cdot b^{-1} \cdot c = a^{-1} \cdot c \in S$.

Thus G is partitioned into disjoint equivalence classes by the relation α. An equivalence class $[a]$ is

$$[a] = \{b \mid a^{-1} \cdot b \in S\} = \{b \mid b = a \cdot c \text{ where } c \in S\} = a \cdot S.$$

This proves (i) for the case of left cosets, and the proof for right cosets is similar.

Now we prove (ii). The function f from S to a particular left coset $a \cdot S$ defined by

$$f(b) = a \cdot b$$

is easily seen to be a bijection. Therefore each left coset of S contains exactly n elements. The left cosets are pairwise-disjoint and so, if there are p of them, their union G contains exactly $pn = m$ elements. The proof for right cosets is similar. $\square$

This theorem has two interesting and immediate corollaries:

(i) *The order of an element of a group divides the order of the group.*

Proof. The result is trivial if the order of the element or the order of the group is 0. If an element has non-0 order n, then the subgroup generated by it contains exactly n elements, by Theorem 5; and so, if the group is finite, n divides the order of the group. $\square$

(ii) *A group of prime order is cyclic.*

Proof. If $(G, \cdot)$ has prime order m, then the order of $a \in G$ is either 1 or m, by the preceding result. If a is not the group identity, then its order is m, and so it generates the group. $\square$

EXERCISES

1. Find all the homomorphic images of the cyclic groups of order 4, 5, and 0.

2. Show that a homomorphism is injective if and only if its kernel contains only the identity element.

3. Show that a subgroup is normal if and only if each of its right cosets is a left coset.

4. Show that the intersection and product of two normal subgroups are normal subgroups.

5. An isomorphism from a group G to G is called an *automorphism* of G. An *inner automorphism* of G is a function f from G to G such that $f(a) = b^{-1} \cdot a \cdot b$ for all $a \in G$ and some fixed $b \in G$. Show that:
(i) the set of all automorphisms of G is a subgroup of the group of all bijections from G to G;
(ii) the set of all inner automorphisms of G is a subgroup of the group of all automorphisms of G;
(iii) a subgroup S of G is normal if and only if $f(S) = S$ for all inner automorphisms f of G.

6. Show that the difference group of $(\mathbf{C}, +)$ by $(\mathbf{R}, +)$ is isomorphic to $(\mathbf{R}, +)$.

7. Let G be the group of all non-0 complex numbers under multiplication, and let H be the subgroup of all positive real numbers. Show that G/H is isomorphic to the group of those complex numbers whose absolute value is 1, under multiplication.

8. Let A be the set of all those elements in a commutative group G which have non-0 order. Show that A is a subgroup of G, and that the elements of G/A have order 0 or 1.

9. Show that if a group of order 4 is not cyclic, then it is isomorphic to the Klein 4-group (p. 85). Show that if a group contains 5 elements or less, then it is commutative.

10. Show that if a group of order 6 is not cyclic, then it is isomorphic to S_3.

11. Let H be a finite subgroup of a cyclic group G. Show that G/H is cyclic, and that its order is the order of G divided by the order of H.

12. If G is a group of order p^n, where p is a prime integer, show that G contains a subgroup of order p.

13. Let G be a finite group, let p be a prime integer, and let S be the set of those elements in G which have order p. Show that the relation 'a is a power of b' is an equivalence relation on S. Deduce that the number of elements in S is divisible by $p - 1$.

Show that a group of order $5p$ contains elements of order p if $p \equiv 3$ (4) and contains elements of order 5 if $p \geqslant 5$.

14. Let S be a subgroup of a finite group G. The number of right (or, equivalently, left) cosets of S is called the *index* of S. Show that if the index of S is 2, then S is normal. Deduce that A_n is a normal subgroup of S_n.

15. Let n be a positive integer, and let G be a group such that $(a \cdot b)^n = a^n \cdot b^n$ for all $a, b \in G$. Let

$$A = \{a \mid a = b^n \text{ for some } b \in G\}$$

and $$B = \{a \mid a^n \text{ is the identity of the group}\}.$$

Show that A and B are subgroups of G and that, if G is finite, then the index of B is the order of A.

16. Let m and n be positive integers, let G be a group of order mn, and let K be a subset of G which contains exactly m elements. Prove that, if there are exactly n right cosets of K, then one of these right cosets is a subgroup of G.

17. Let G be a group, let $a \in G$, and let $N = \{b \mid a \cdot b = b \cdot a\}$. Show that N is a subgroup of G, and that the function f defined by

$$f(N \cdot g) = g^{-1} \cdot a \cdot g$$

is an injection from the set of all right cosets of N to G. Hence show that, if G is S_4 and $a = (1, 2) \circ (3, 4)$, then the order of N is 8.

6   Rings and fields

In the first two chapters we constructed sets that were subject to two binary operations, addition and multiplication. They were groups under addition, but not under multiplication since the additive identity 0 did not have a multiplicative inverse. Now we will consider sets which are subject to two binary operations and impose on them conditions suggested by the theorems we proved in Chapters 1 and 2.

DEFINITION. A *ring* is a set G and two binary operations $+$ and $\cdot$ on G with the properties:
(i) $(G, +)$ is a commutative group;
(ii) the operation $\cdot$ is closed and associative;
(iii) if $a, b, c \in G$, then $a \cdot (b + c) = (a \cdot b) + (a \cdot c)$ and $(b + c) \cdot a = (b \cdot a) + (c \cdot a)$.

A ring will be denoted by a symbol like $(G, +, \cdot)$, where G is the set, $+$ is the group operation on G, and $\cdot$ is the closed and associative operation on G. We will commit our usual misuse of terms: G may sometimes be referred to as the ring and the elements of G referred to as the elements of the ring. The identity of the group $(G, +)$ will usually be denoted by 0 and the inverse of $a \in G$ by $-a$. Property (iii) is called the *distributive law*, and the operation $\cdot$ is said to be *distributive with respect to the operation* $+$ if (iii) holds.

DEFINITIONS. A ring $(G, +, \cdot)$ is:

(i) *commutative* if $a \cdot b = b \cdot a$ for all $a, b \in G$;

(ii) a *ring with identity* if there is an element $I \in G$ such that $a \cdot I = I \cdot a = a$ for all $a \in G$ – such an element is called an *identity* of the ring;

(iii) an *integral domain* if it is a commutative ring with identity and has the property: if $a, b \in G$ and $a \cdot b = 0$, then at least one of a, b is 0;

(iv) a *field* if the set $G - \{0\}$, that is, G with the identity of the group $(G, +)$ omitted, is a commutative group under the operation $\cdot$. If $(G, +, \cdot)$ is a field, then $(G, +)$ is the *additive group* and $(G - \{0\}, \cdot)$ is the *multiplicative group* of the field.

EXAMPLES. (i) $(\mathbf{Q}, +, \cdot)$, $(\mathbf{R}, +, \cdot)$, and $(\mathbf{C}, +, \cdot)$ are fields.

(ii) The set of all even integers is a commutative ring without an identity, under the usual operations.

(iii) $(\mathbf{Z}, +, \cdot)$ is an integral domain but is not a field.

(iv) The set of all residue classes modulo n is a commutative ring with identity, under the usual operations. It is a field if and only if n is a prime integer and $n \neq \pm 1$. The required properties were shown to hold in Theorem 21, p. 31, and Example (iii), p. 66.

(v) If $(G, +)$ is a commutative group, and $a \cdot b$ is defined to be 0 for all $a, b \in G$, then it is easily seen that $(G, +, \cdot)$ is a commutative ring. Such a ring is called a *zero ring*.

(vi) Let A be a set, let $(G, +, \cdot)$ be a ring, and let K be the set of all functions from A to G. Define the operations $+$ and $\cdot$ on K by

$$(f + g)(x) = f(x) + g(x) \text{ for all } x \in A$$

and $$(f \cdot g)(x) = f(x) \cdot g(x) \text{ for all } x \in A.$$

Then $(K, +, \cdot)$ is a ring. The closure and associativity of the operations, and the distributive law, follow from the corresponding properties of $(G, +, \cdot)$. The function in K that associates the identity of G with every element of A is the identity of $(K, +)$, and the inverse for $f \in K$ is the function $-f$ defined by

$$-f(x) = -(f(x))$$

for all $x \in A$.

DEFINITION. An element a of a ring $(G, +, \cdot)$ is a *divisor of 0* if $a \neq 0$ and there is an element $b \in G$ such that $b \neq 0$ and either $a \cdot b = 0$ or $b \cdot a = 0$.

EXAMPLE. The ring of residue classes modulo 4 is a ring with divisors of 0, since $[2] \cdot [2] = [0]$ and $[2] \neq [0]$.

By definition, an integral domain is just a commutative ring with identity which contains no divisors of 0.

If $(G, +, \cdot)$ is a ring and $a \in G$, then

$$a \cdot 0 = a \cdot (0 + 0) = (a \cdot 0) + (a \cdot 0)$$

and so $a \cdot 0 = 0$. Similarly, $0 \cdot a = 0$. If $(G, +, \cdot)$ is a field, then the operation $\cdot$ is commutative because if $a, b \in G$ and neither a nor b are 0 then they are both in the commutative group $(G - \{0\}, \cdot)$, and if one of them is 0 then $a \cdot b = 0 = b \cdot a$, as we have just seen. Also, if $a \cdot b = 0$ and $a \neq 0$, then, since a has a multiplicative inverse a^{-1},

$$b = a^{-1} \cdot a \cdot b = a^{-1} \cdot 0 = 0.$$

Similarly, if $a \cdot b = 0$ and $b \neq 0$, then $a = 0$. Thus a field is an integral domain.

DEFINITIONS. A *subring* of a ring $(G, +, \cdot)$ is a subset of G which is a ring under the operations $+$ and $\cdot$. A *subfield* is a subring which is a field.

Here we are committing our usual misuse of terms. To be precise, a subring of a ring $(G, +, \cdot)$ is a ring $(H, \oplus, \odot)$ such that:
(i) H is a subset of G;
(ii) $a + b = a \oplus b$ and $a \cdot b = a \odot b$, for all $a, b \in H$.

We note that a subring of a field need not be a subfield: $(\mathbf{Z}, +, \cdot)$ is a subring of the field $(\mathbf{R}, +, \cdot)$, but is not a subfield. However, a subring of a field clearly must be commutative and cannot contain any divisors of 0.

DEFINITIONS. Let $(G, +, \cdot)$ and $(H, \oplus, \odot)$ be rings. A *homomorphism from* $(G, +, \cdot)$ *to* $(H, \oplus, \odot)$ is a homomorphism f from $(G, +)$ to $(H, \oplus)$ such that $f(a \cdot b) = f(a) \odot f(b)$ for all $a, b \in G$. An *isomorphism from* $(G, +, \cdot)$ *to* $(H, \oplus, \odot)$ is a bijective homomorphism from $(G, +, \cdot)$ to $(H, \oplus, \odot)$.

In Chapters 1 and 2 we proved that the functions given in Example (i), p. 81, were injective ring homomorphisms.

THEOREM 18. *If f is a homomorphism from a ring $(G, +, \cdot)$ to a ring $(H, \oplus, \odot)$, then:*
(i) $f(0) = 0'$, *where $0, 0'$ are the identities of $(G, +)$, $(H, \oplus)$ respectively;*
(ii) $f(-a) = -f(a)$ *for all $a \in G$, where $-a$ and $-f(a)$ are the additive inverses of a and $f(a)$;*
(iii) $f(G)$ *is a subring of H;*
(iv) *if G is a commutative ring, then $f(G)$ is a commutative subring of H;*
(v) *if G has a multiplicative identity I, then $f(I)$ is a multiplicative identity for $f(G)$;*
(vi) *if f is an injection, then it is an isomorphism from $(G, +, \cdot)$ to $(f(G), \oplus, \odot)$;*
(vii) *if f is an injection and H is a field, then G is a commutative ring with no divisors of 0.*

Proof. (i) and (ii) were proved in Theorem 13. By (iii) of that theorem, $(f(G), \oplus)$ is a subgroup of $(H, \oplus)$, and so, to prove (iii), we need only show that if $a, b \in G$ then $f(a) \odot f(b) \in f(G)$. This follows from $f(a) \odot f(b) = f(a \cdot b)$, and (iv) and (v) also follow immediately from this equality. (vi) follows immediately from (iii) and the definition of the term 'isomorphism'.

If H is a field, then $f(G)$ is a subring of a field, and hence is commutative and contains no divisors of 0. If, further, f is an injection and $a, b \in G$, then $f(a \cdot b) = f(a) \odot f(b) = f(b) \odot f(a) = f(b \cdot a)$, and so $a \cdot b = b \cdot a$. If $a \cdot b = 0$, then $f(a) \odot f(b) = f(0) = 0'$, and so one of $f(a)$, $f(b)$ is $0'$. If $f(a) = 0'$, then $a = 0$ because f is an injection and $f(0) = 0'$. Similarly, if $f(b) = 0'$, then $b = 0$. □

If f is an injective homomorphism from a ring $(G, +, \cdot)$ to a ring $(H, \oplus, \odot)$, then, by the above theorem, $f(G)$ is a subring of H and f is an isomorphism from G to $f(G)$. As in the case of groups, isomorphic rings are regarded as algebraically identical, and so G and $f(G)$ can be regarded as being the same ring. We say that G is *embedded* in H by the injective homomorphism f. By part (vii) of the above theorem, if a ring can be embedded in a field, then it is necessarily a commutative ring with no divisors of 0. We now prove the converse of this statement.

THEOREM 19. *A commutative ring with no divisors of 0 can be embedded in a field.*

Proof. Let $(G, +, \cdot)$ be a commutative ring with no divisors of 0. If G contains only one element, 0, then it clearly can be embedded in any field, so we assume that G contains a non-0 element. We now proceed as we did at the beginning of Chapter 2, where we embedded the ring of integers $(\mathbf{Z}, +, \cdot)$ in the ring of rational numbers $(\mathbf{Q}, +, \cdot)$. Let $A = \{\langle a, b \rangle \mid a, b \in G \text{ and } b \neq 0\}$, and let α be the relation defined on A by '$\langle a, b \rangle \, \alpha \, \langle d, e \rangle$ if and only if $a \cdot e = b \cdot d$'. This relation is an equivalence relation. Let F be the set of equivalence classes, and let $\oplus$ and $\odot$ be the binary operations defined on F by

$$[\langle a, b \rangle] \oplus [\langle d, e \rangle] = [\langle a \cdot e + b \cdot d, b \cdot e \rangle],$$
$$[\langle a, b \rangle] \odot [\langle d, e \rangle] = [\langle a \cdot d, b \cdot e \rangle].$$

Then $(F, \oplus, \odot)$ is a field. Let c be a non-0 element of G – there is such an element by our assumption – and define the function f from G to F by

$$f(a) = [\langle c \cdot a, c \rangle].$$

Then f is an injective homomorphism from $(G, +, \cdot)$ to $(F, \oplus, \odot)$.

The details of the proof are left to the reader. They are easy generalizations of our remarks on pp. 37–39. □

In the last section, we saw that the homomorphisms from a group are completely determined by its normal subgroups, each of which is a kernel for some homomorphism. The situation is much the same for rings. If f is a homomorphism from a ring $(G, +, \cdot)$ to a ring $(H, \oplus, \odot)$, then it is a homomorphism from the group $(G, +)$ to the group $(H, \oplus)$, and so, by our previous remarks, it is completely determined by its kernel $K = \{x \mid x \in G$ and $f(x)$ is the identity of $(H, \oplus)\}$. We have already shown that K is a normal subgroup of G. Note that the normality of K is of no interest, since G is a commutative group. Also, if $a \in K$ and $b \in G$, then

$$f(a \cdot b) = f(a) \odot f(b) = 0 \odot f(b) = 0,$$

and similarly $f(b \cdot a) = 0$, where 0 is the identity of $(H, \oplus)$. That is, if $a \in K$ and $b \in G$, then $a \cdot b \in K$ and $b \cdot a \in K$.

DEFINITION. An *ideal* of a ring $(G, +, \cdot)$ is a subgroup $(K, +)$ of the group $(G, +)$ with the property: if $a \in K$ and $b \in G$, then $a \cdot b \in K$ and $b \cdot a \in K$.

We have just seen that the kernel of a ring homomorphism is an ideal. Now we prove the converse.

THEOREM 20. *Let K be an ideal of a ring $(G, +, \cdot)$, and let $(G - K, \oplus)$ be the difference group of $(G, +)$ by $(K, +)$. If $(K + a) \odot (K + b)$ is defined to be $K + (a \cdot b)$, for all $K + a$, $K + b \in G - K$, then $(G - K, \oplus, \odot)$ is a ring. The canonical homomorphism from $(G, +)$ induced by K is a surjective homomorphism from $(G, +, \cdot)$ to $(G - K, \oplus, \odot)$, with kernel K.*

Proof. Since K is a subgroup of a commutative group G, it is a normal subgroup of G, and hence the difference group $(G - K, \oplus)$ exists. The commutativity of $G - K$ follows immediately from the commutativity of G.

The proof that $\odot$ is a binary operation on $G - K$ is identical to the first part of the proof of Theorem 16. If $a, b, c \in G$, then

$$(K + a) \odot ((K + b) \odot (K + c)) = (K + a) \odot (K + b \cdot c)$$
$$= K + a \cdot (b \cdot c),$$

and similarly

$$((K + a) \odot (K + b)) \odot (K + c) = K + (a \cdot b) \cdot c.$$

Thus the associativity of the operation $\odot$ follows from the associativity of $\cdot$, and similarly the distributive law for $(G - K, \oplus, \odot)$ follows from the distributive law for $(G, +, \cdot)$. Thus $(G - K, \oplus, \odot)$ is a ring.

We saw in the last section that the canonical homomorphism

$$f(a) = K + a$$

is a surjective homomorphism from $(G, +)$ to $(G - K, \oplus)$, with kernel K. It only remains to show that

$$f(a \cdot b) = f(a) \odot f(b)$$

for all a, $b \in G$, and this follows immediately from the definition of $\odot$. □

DEFINITION. Let $(K, +)$ be an ideal of a ring $(G, +, \cdot)$. Let $(G - K, \oplus)$ be the difference group of $(G, +)$ by $(K, +)$, and let $\odot$ be the binary operation defined on $G - K$ by

$$(K + a) \odot (K + b) = K + (a \cdot b)$$

for all $K + a$, $K + b \in G - K$. The ring $(G - K, \oplus, \odot)$ is the *difference ring of G by K*.

We noted on p. 90 that the additive groups of residue classes and the additive group of real numbers were constructed as difference groups. Now, considering both addition and multiplication, it should be apparent that these sets were in fact constructed as difference rings.

EXERCISES

1. Let $(K, +, \cdot)$ be the ring of all functions from **R** to **R**, as defined in Example (vi), p. 94. Determine the algebraic structure of each of the following subsets of K:
   (i) $\{f \mid f(x) = f(y) \text{ for all } x, y \in \mathbf{R}\}$, (ii) $\{f \mid f(x) = -f(-x) \text{ for all } x \in \mathbf{R}\}$,
   (iii) $\{f \mid f(x) = f(-x) \text{ for all } x \in \mathbf{R}\}$, (iv) $\{f \mid f(x) = x \cdot f(1) \text{ for all } x \in \mathbf{R}\}$,
   (v) $\{f \mid f(x + y) = f(x) + f(y) \text{ for all } x, y \in \mathbf{R}\}$.

2. Show that, if a, b, c, d are elements of a ring $(G, +, \cdot)$, then:
(i) $-(a \cdot b) = (-a) \cdot b = a \cdot (-b)$;
(ii) $a \cdot (b - c) = (a \cdot b) - (a \cdot c)$;
(iii) $(-a) \cdot (-b) = a \cdot b$.
   If G has an identity I, show that:
(iv) I is unique;
(v) $(-I) \cdot a = -a$.
   If G is a field, show that:
(vi) $a \cdot b^{-1} - c \cdot d^{-1} = (a \cdot d - b \cdot c) \cdot (b \cdot d)^{-1}$;
(vii) $(-a)^{-1} = -(a^{-1})$;
(viii) $-a \cdot (-b)^{-1} = a \cdot b^{-1}$.

3. Show that, if $(G, +)$ is a group which contains more than one element, then $(G, +, +)$ is not a ring.

4. If $(G, +, \cdot)$ is a field, can $(G, \cdot, +)$ also be a field?

5. Let $(G, +)$ be a commutative group, and let $\cdot$ be a closed and associative operation on G such that

$$(a + b) \cdot (c + d) = a \cdot c + b \cdot c + a \cdot d + b \cdot d$$

for all a, b, c, $d \in G$. Show that $(G, +, \cdot)$ need not be a ring.

6. Show that, if an integral domain contains at least two elements, but not an infinite number, then it is a field.

7. Show that a subset A of a ring is a subring if and only if it is not empty and, whenever $a, b \in A$, then $a - b, a \cdot b \in A$.

8. Show that the additive and multiplicative groups of a field cannot be isomorphic.

9. Show that a homomorphic image of an integral domain need not be an integral domain.

10. Let $(G, +, \cdot)$ be a ring, let H be the set of all ordered pairs of elements of G, and let $\oplus$ and $\odot$ be the binary operations defined on H by
$$\langle a, b \rangle \oplus \langle c, d \rangle = \langle a + c, b + d \rangle,$$
$$\langle a, b \rangle \odot \langle c, d \rangle = \langle a \cdot c, b \cdot d \rangle.$$
Show that $(H, \oplus, \odot)$ is a ring, and that if $(G, +, \cdot)$ is a commutative ring with identity then so is $(H, \oplus, \odot)$. Also, show that $(H, \oplus, \odot)$ is not an integral domain, except in a trivial case.

Find an example of a ring with identity which contains a subring with identity, such that these two identities are not the same element.

11. Let $(G, +, \cdot)$ be a field, let H be the set of all ordered pairs of elements of G, and let $\oplus$ and $\odot$ be the binary operations defined on H by
$$\langle a, b \rangle \oplus \langle c, d \rangle = \langle a + c, b + d \rangle,$$
$$\langle a, b \rangle \odot \langle c, d \rangle = \langle a \cdot c, 0 \rangle.$$
Show that $(H, \oplus, \odot)$ is a ring without an identity which contains a subfield.

12. Let $(G, +, \cdot)$ be a ring and let H be the set of all ordered pairs $\langle n, a \rangle$, where $n \in \mathbf{Z}$ and $a \in G$. Let $\oplus$ and $\odot$ be the binary operations defined on H by
$$\langle n, a \rangle \oplus \langle m, b \rangle = \langle n + m, a + b \rangle,$$
$$\langle n, a \rangle \odot \langle m, b \rangle = \langle nm, nb + ma + a \cdot b \rangle.$$
Show, by considering $(H, \oplus, \odot)$, that every ring can be embedded in a ring with identity.

13. Let G be a subring of a field K, and let F be the field obtained in Theorem 19 in which G can be embedded. Show that F can be embedded in K.

14. Show that a field G has only two ideals, G itself and the set containing only the additive identity. Deduce that there are only two homomorphisms from G to a ring.

15. Let H and K be ideals of a commutative ring $(G, +, \cdot)$, and let $a \in G$. Show that $H + K$ and $a \cdot H$ are ideals of G.

16. Let K be an ideal of a ring G. Show that:
(i) if G has an identity, then so has $G - K$;
(ii) if G is commutative and has an identity, then $G - K$ is an integral domain if and only if, whenever $a, b \in G$ and $a \cdot b \in K$, then at least one of a, b is in K;
(iii) if G is commutative and has an identity, then $G - K$ is a field if and only if G contains an element which is not in K and, whenever D is an ideal of G such that $K \subseteq D$, then either $D = K$ or $D = G$.

17. Let G be a field which contains just a finite number of elements. Show that there is a prime integer p such that $px = 0$ for all $x \in G$.

18. Let G be a non-empty set, and let $\circ$ be an associative binary operation on G with the properties:

(i) there is an element $I \in G$ such that $b \circ I = I \circ b = b$ for all $b \in G$;

(ii) there is an element $a \in G$ such that, if $b \neq a$ and $b \in G$, then there is an element $c \in G$ such that $b \circ c = I$.

Show that $a \circ x = x \circ a = a$ for all $x \in G$.

If $(G, +, \cdot)$ is a ring and the three operations $+$, $\cdot$ and $\circ$ are connected by the law

$$x \circ y = x + y + x \cdot y,$$

show that I is the additive identity of G. Prove also that

$$x + a \cdot x = x + x \cdot a = I$$

for all $x \in G$, and hence that $-a$ is the multiplicative identity of G.

7 Ordered groups and rings

DEFINITIONS. (i) A set A is *totally ordered* by a relation $\leqslant$ if $\leqslant$ is a relation on A with the properties:

(a) if $a, b \in A$, then either $a \leqslant b$ or $b \leqslant a$;

(b) if $a, b \in A$ and both $a \leqslant b$ and $b \leqslant a$ hold, then $a = b$;

(c) if $a, b, c \in A$, $a \leqslant b$, and $b \leqslant c$, then $a \leqslant c$.

(ii) A *totally ordered group* is a group $(G, +)$ and a relation $\leqslant$ on G such that G is totally ordered by $\leqslant$ and, if $a, b, c \in G$ and $a \leqslant b$, then $a + c \leqslant b + c$ and $c + a \leqslant c + b$. We will denote such a totally ordered group by $(G, +, \leqslant)$.

(iii) A *totally ordered ring* is a ring $(G, +, \cdot)$ and a relation $\leqslant$ on G such that $(G, +, \leqslant)$ is a totally ordered group and, if $a, b, c \in G$, $a \leqslant b$, and $0 \leqslant c$, then $a \cdot c \leqslant b \cdot c$ and $c \cdot a \leqslant c \cdot b$. We will denote such a totally ordered ring by $(G, +, \cdot, \leqslant)$.

(iv) A *totally ordered field* is a totally ordered ring $(G, +, \cdot, \leqslant)$ such that $(G, +, \cdot)$ is a field.

EXAMPLES. (i) The field of real numbers $(\mathbf{R}, +, \cdot)$, with the usual order, is a totally ordered field.

(ii) The group of non-0 real numbers under multiplication, with the usual order, is not a totally ordered group. For example, $1 \leqslant 2$, but $-1 \cdot 1 > -1 \cdot 2$. The group of positive real numbers under multiplication, with the usual order, is a totally ordered group.

(iii) $(\mathbf{C}, +, \leqslant:)$ is a totally ordered group if $\leqslant:$ is defined on $\mathbf{C}$ by: $a + ib \leqslant: c + id$, where a, b, c, d are real numbers, if and only if, either $c > a$ or $c = a$ and $d \geqslant b$. It is easy to see that $(\mathbf{C}, +, \cdot, \leqslant:)$ is not a totally ordered field.

(iv) Let $(G, +, \leqslant)$ be a totally ordered group, and let $\geqslant$ be the relation defined on G by: $a \geqslant b$ if and only if $b \leqslant a$. Then $(G, +, \geqslant)$ is a totally ordered group.

DEFINITION. An isomorphism f from a totally ordered group $(G, +, \leqslant)$ to a totally ordered group $(H, \oplus, \leqslant:)$, or from a totally ordered ring $(G, +, \cdot, \leqslant)$ to a totally ordered ring $(H, \oplus, \odot, \leqslant:)$, is an *order-isomorphism* if, whenever $a, b \in G$ and $a \leqslant b$, then $f(a) \leqslant: f(b)$.

It is easy to verify that the relation of being order-isomorphic is an equivalence relation between totally ordered groups. The next theorem characterizes those totally ordered groups which are order-isomorphic to some subgroup of $(\mathbf{R}, +, \leqslant)$.

DEFINITION. A totally ordered group $(G, +, \leqslant)$ or ring $(G, +, \cdot, \leqslant)$ is *archimedean* if, for every ordered pair $\langle a, b \rangle$ of elements from G with $a \neq 0$, there is an integer n such that $b \leqslant na$.

EXAMPLES. (i) The field $(\mathbf{R}, +, \cdot, \leqslant)$ is archimedean; see Theorem 4(iv), p. 47.

(ii) The group of positive real numbers under multiplication, with the usual order, is an archimedean totally ordered group. This follows from Exercise 8, p. 48.

(iii) The totally ordered group $(\mathbf{C}, +, \leqslant:)$, as defined in Example (iii) above, is not archimedean. For example, $ni \leqslant: 1$ for all integers n.

Every subgroup of an archimedean totally ordered group is necessarily an archimedean totally ordered group and so, in particular, every subgroup of $(\mathbf{R}, +, \leqslant)$ is archimedean totally ordered. The next theorem is just the converse of this statement. It was proved by O. Hölder in 1901.

In the proofs of the remaining two theorems of this section we will use the results of Exercise 1, p. 106, and the reader may prefer to verify these results before proceeding further.

THEOREM 21. *Every archimedean totally ordered group is order-isomorphic to a subgroup of* $(\mathbf{R}, +, \leqslant)$.

Proof. Let $(H, \oplus, \leqslant:)$ be an archimedean totally ordered group. If H contains only one element, then it is clearly order-isomorphic to a subgroup of $\mathbf{R}$; and so we assume that H contains a non-0 element a. If $a \leqslant: 0$, then $0 \leqslant: -a$, and so we can assume that $0 \leqslant: a$. This non-0 element $a \in H$ such that $0 \leqslant: a$ will be fixed throughout the remainder of the proof.

For each $x \in H$, let $f(x)$ be the least upper bound of the following set of rational numbers

$$\{t/s \mid t, s \text{ are integers}, s > 0, \text{ and } 0 \leqslant: sx - ta\}.$$

We will show that f is an order-isomorphism from H to a subgroup of **R**.

(i) We first show that f is a function from H to **R**. Let $x \in H$. We must show that $f(x)$ is defined, that is, we must show that the set by which we define $f(x)$ is not empty and is bounded above. If $0 \leqslant: x$, then $0 \leqslant: 1x - 0a$. If $x \leqslant: 0$, then, by the archimedean property, there is an integer $-t$ such that $-x \leqslant: -ta$, from which $0 \leqslant: 1x - ta$. Thus the relevant set is not empty. Suppose that t and s are integers such that $s > 0$ and $0 \leqslant: sx - ta$, and let n be an integer such that $x \leqslant: na$. Then

$$ta \leqslant: sx \leqslant: sna,$$

and so $t/s \leqslant n$. Thus the set by which we define $f(x)$ is bounded above. Therefore $f(x)$ exists.

(ii) Let x and y be elements of H such that $x \oplus y \leqslant: y \oplus x$. We will show that $f(x) + f(y) \leqslant f(x \oplus y)$. Let ϵ be a positive real number, and let s, s' be positive integers and t, t' integers such that

$$
\begin{aligned}
0 &\leqslant: s'x - t'a, \\
0 &\leqslant: sy - ta, \\
t'/s' &> f(x) - \epsilon, \\
t/s &> f(y) - \epsilon.
\end{aligned}
$$

There are such integers, since $f(x)$ and $f(y)$ exist. From these inequalities, we get $st'a \leqslant: ss'x$ and $s'ta \leqslant: s's y$, so·that

$$(st' + s't)a \leqslant: ss'x \oplus s'sy.$$

From $x \oplus y \leqslant: y \oplus x$ it follows, by a simple induction argument, that $nx \oplus ny \leqslant: n(x \oplus y)$ for all positive integers n, and so

$$(st' + s't)a \leqslant: ss'(x \oplus y).$$

Thus

$$f(x \oplus y) \geqslant (st' + s't)/ss' > f(x) + f(y) - 2\epsilon.$$

Since $f(x \oplus y)$, $f(x)$, and $f(y)$ do not depend on ϵ, we have the required result.

(iii) If $x \leqslant: y$, then

$$\{t/s \,|\, t, s \text{ are integers}, s > 0, \text{ and } 0 \leqslant: sx - ta\} \subseteq$$
$$\{t/s \,|\, t, s \text{ are integers}, s > 0, \text{ and } 0 \leqslant: sy - ta\}.$$

Since an upper bound for the larger set is also an upper bound for the smaller set, we have $f(x) \leqslant f(y)$.

(iv) From (ii) and (iii),

$$f(x) + f(y) \leqslant f(x \oplus y)$$

for all $x, y \in H$. Also, it is easy to verify that $f(0) = 0$, and so

$$0 = f(0) \geqslant f(x) + f(-x).$$

Thus, $f(x) \leqslant -f(-x)$ for all $x \in H$.

(v) Now we will show that $f(x) = -f(-x)$ for all $x \in H$. Let $x \in H$ and let s be a positive integer. By the archimedean property of $\leqslant:$, there is an integer t such that $0 \leqslant: sx - ta$ and $sx - (t+1)a \leqslant: 0$. Then $f(x) \geqslant t/s$ and $f(-x) \geqslant -(t+1)/s$, so that

$$f(x) + f(-x) \geqslant -1/s.$$

But s is an arbitrary positive integer, and so $f(x) + f(-x) \geqslant 0$. This, with (iv), gives the required result.

(vi) If $x, y \in H$, then, by (v) and (ii),

$$\begin{aligned} -f(x \oplus y) &= f(-(x \oplus y)) \\ &= f(-y - x) \\ &\geqslant f(-y) + f(-x) = -f(y) - f(x). \end{aligned}$$

This, with (iv), proves that f is a homomorphism.

(vii) Let x and y be different elements of H. We can assume, by symmetry, that $0 \leqslant: x - y$. Since $\leqslant:$ is archimedean, there is an integer $n > 0$ such that $0 \leqslant: n(x - y) - a$, and so

$$f(x) - f(y) = f(x - y) \geqslant 1/n > 0.$$

Thus, f is an injection.

We have now shown that f is an injective homomorphism from $(H, \oplus)$ to $(\mathbf{R}, +)$, and thus, by Theorem 13(iv), f is an isomorphism from $(H, \oplus)$ to a subgroup of $(\mathbf{R}, +)$. That it is an order-isomorphism follows immediately from (iii). $\square$

The order-isomorphism f obtained in the above proof clearly depends on the chosen element a. This lack of uniqueness is to be expected, since cf, where c is any positive real number, is also an order-isomorphism from H to a subgroup of $\mathbf{R}$. We now show that every order-isomorphism from H to a subgroup of $\mathbf{R}$ is of this form.

THEOREM 22. *Let f and g be injective homomorphisms from a totally ordered group $(H, \oplus, \leqslant:)$ to $(\mathbf{R}, +, \leqslant)$, with the property that, if $x, y \in H$ and $x \leqslant: y$, then $f(x) \leqslant f(y)$ and $g(x) \leqslant g(y)$. Then there is a positive real number c such that $f(x) = cg(x)$ for all $x \in H$.*

Proof. It is sufficient to show, that if $x, y \in H$ and $x \neq 0$, then

$$g(y)/g(x) = f(y)/f(x).$$

For, if this can be shown, then $f(y) = cg(y)$, where $c = f(x)/g(x)$, and c is clearly positive by the conditions on f and g.

Suppose, then, that

$$g(y)/g(x) < f(y)/f(x)$$

for some $x, y \in H$, $x \neq 0$. Since there is a rational number between any two different real numbers, there are integers s and t such that $t > 0$ and

$$g(y)/g(x) < s/t < f(y)/f(x).$$

If $0 \leqslant: x$, then we have

$$g(ty) = tg(y) < sg(x) = g(sx)$$

and $$f(sx) = sf(x) < tf(y) = f(ty).$$

But this is impossible, by the conditions on f and g, and so we have a contradiction. Similar contradictions are obtained if $x \leqslant: 0$ or if $f(y)/f(x) < g(y)/g(x)$. □

We have already noted that the group of positive real numbers under multiplication, with the usual order, is an archimedean totally ordered group. Thus, by the above two theorems, there is a unique function f from the set of positive real numbers to **R** such that:

(i) $f(xy) = f(x) + f(y)$ for all positive real numbers x, y;
(ii) if $0 < x < y$, then $f(x) < f(y)$;
(iii) $f(a) = 1$, where a is a fixed real number greater than 1.

This function is a familiar one, $\log_a (x)$. Since it is uniquely defined by the above three conditions, all its properties, and those of the corresponding exponential function a^x, should be deducible from these conditions. The proofs of some of these properties are set as exercises.

DEFINITIONS. Let a set G be totally ordered by a relation $\leqslant:$, and let A be a subset of G. An element $a \in G$ is a *lower bound* for A if $a \leqslant: b$ for all $b \in A$. If A has a lower bound, then A is *bounded below*. An element $a \in G$ is a *greatest lower bound* for A if it is a lower bound for A, and $b \leqslant: a$ for all lower bounds b for A.

In Theorem 8 of Chapter 2, we proved that every non-empty set of real numbers which is bounded below has a greatest lower bound, and we remarked that this property is sometimes taken as a postulate in real analysis. We have also shown that $(\mathbf{R}, +, \cdot, \leqslant)$ is a totally ordered field. Now we will prove that these two properties completely characterize the field of real numbers.

THEOREM 23. *Let $(G, \oplus, \odot, \leqslant:)$ be a totally ordered field with the* *property that every non-empty subset of G which is bounded below has a greatest lower bound. Then $(G, \oplus, \odot, \leqslant:)$ is order-isomorphic to $(\mathbf{R}, +, \cdot, \leqslant)$.*

Proof. First we show that $(G, \oplus, \leqslant:)$ is an archimedean totally ordered group. If this is not the case, then there are elements $a, b \in G$ such that $a \neq 0$ and $na \leqslant: b$ for all $n \in \mathbf{Z}$. Fix such an element a, and let c be a greatest lower bound for the set $T = \{b \mid b \in G$ and $na \leqslant: b$ for all $n \in \mathbf{Z}\}$. We have assumed that T is not empty. It is clearly bounded below, and so, by the condition of the theorem, c exists. Suppose that $0 \leqslant: a$. Then $c \oplus a$ is not a lower bound for T, and thus there is an element $b \in T$ such that $b \leqslant: c \oplus a$. For every integer n,

$$na = (n+2)a - 2a \leqslant: b - 2a \leqslant: c - a.$$

Therefore $c - a \in T$. This is a contradiction, since c is a lower bound for T. If $a \leqslant: 0$, then a contradiction is obtained if a is replaced by $-a$ in the above argument. Thus $(G, \oplus, \leqslant:)$ is an archimedean totally ordered group.

Therefore, by Theorem 21, there is an order-isomorphism f from $(G, \oplus, \leqslant:)$ to a subgroup $f(G)$ of $(\mathbf{R}, +, \leqslant:)$. Let the multiplicative identity of the field $(G, \oplus, \odot)$ be denoted by I. It is easy to see that, because $I = I \odot I$, we must have $0 \leqslant: I$. Therefore, by the remark preceding Theorem 22, we can choose f so that $f(I) = 1$. Making this choice, we then have $f(I \oplus I) = 2$, $f(-I) = -1$, etc., so that $\mathbf{Z} \subseteq f(G)$. Now let n and m be integers, $m > 0$. Then $mI \neq 0$, because G is a totally ordered group, and so, because G is a field, there is an element $d \in G$ such that $mI \odot d = nI$. It follows from this that $f(d) = n/m$. Thus $\mathbf{Q} \subseteq f(G)$. Now let $r \in \mathbf{R}$, and let $A = \{x \mid x \in G$ and $f(x) \geqslant r\}$. The set A is not empty since every rational number is in $f(G)$, and it is bounded below by nI if n is chosen so that $nf(I) \leqslant r$. Thus A has a greatest lower bound c. If $f(c) < r$, then there is a rational number s such that $f(c) < s < r$, and so, by the preceding result, an element $d \in G$ such that $f(c) < s = f(d) < r$. Since f is an order-isomorphism, $c \leqslant: d$, and d is a lower bound for A. This contradicts the definition of c. A similar argument yields a contradiction if $r < f(c)$, and so $r = f(c)$. Therefore $f(G) = \mathbf{R}$.

It only remains to show that f is a ring homomorphism, that is that $f(b \odot c) = f(b) \cdot f(c)$ for all $b, c \in G$. We will do this in three steps, according as $f(b)$ is an integer, a rational number, or a real number.

Let $b, c \in G$ and suppose that $f(b)$ is an integer. Then $b = f(b)I$, and so

$$f(b) \cdot f(c) = f(f(b)c)$$
$$= f(b \odot c).$$

Now suppose that $f(b) = n/m$, where n, m are integers and $m \neq 0$. Then

$$mf(b) \cdot f(c) = f(mb) \cdot f(c)$$
$$= f(mb \odot c)$$

$$mf(b) \cdot f(c) = f(m(b \odot c))$$
$$= mf(b \odot c),$$

and so $f(b) \cdot f(c) = f(b \odot c)$ if $f(b)$ is a rational number.

Now let b and c be any elements of G such that $f(b \odot c) > f(b) \cdot f(c)$ and $f(c) > 0$. Then there is a rational number ~ which, since $\mathbf{Q} \subseteq f(G)$, we can assume is $f(e)$ for some $e \in G$ – such that

$$f(b \odot c)/f(c) > f(e) > f(b).$$

Since $f(e)$ is rational, $f(e) \cdot f(c) = f(e \odot c)$. Thus

$$f(b \odot c) > f(e \odot c),$$

and so $e \odot c \leqslant: b \odot c$. Since $0 \leqslant: c$ and $c \neq 0$, we therefore have $e \leqslant: b$. But $f(e) > f(b)$, and so we have a contradiction. We have now shown that if $f(c) > 0$, then $f(b \odot c) \leqslant f(b) \cdot f(c)$ for all $b \in G$. The desired result follows easily from this. □

EXERCISES

1. Show that, if $(G, +, \leqslant)$ is a totally ordered group, $a, b, c, d \in G$, $a \leqslant b$, and $c \leqslant d$, then:
(i) $a + c \leqslant b + d$;
(ii) $-b \leqslant -a$;
(iii) if $0 \leqslant a$ and $0 \leqslant -a$, then $0 = a$.

2. Show that, if $(G, +, \cdot, \leqslant)$ is a totally ordered ring, $a, b \in G$, $0 \leqslant a$, and $0 \leqslant b$, then $0 \leqslant a \cdot b$. Show that, if $c \in G$, then $0 \leqslant c^2$, and that $0 = c^2$ if and only if $0 = c$.

3. A set A is *quasi-ordered* by a relation $\leqslant$ if $\leqslant$ is a relation on A with the properties:
(i) if $a, b \in A$, then either $a \leqslant b$ or $b \leqslant a$;
(ii) if $a, b, c \in A$, $a \leqslant b$, and $b \leqslant c$, then $a \leqslant c$.
Show that if a set A is quasi-ordered by $\leqslant$, then the relation α on A defined by '$a \; \alpha \; b$ if and only if $a \leqslant b$ and $b \leqslant a$' is an equivalence relation on A. Show that the set of equivalence classes is totally ordered by the relation $\leqslant:$ defined by '$B \leqslant: C$ if and only if there are elements $a \in B$, $b \in C$, such that $a \leqslant b$'.

4. Let $(G, +, \leqslant)$ be a totally ordered group, and let $P = \{a \mid a \in G$ and $0 \leqslant a\}$. Show that:
(i) $0 \in P$;
(ii) if $a \in P$ and $-a \in P$, then $a = 0$;
(iii) if $a \in G$ and $a \notin P$, then $-a \in P$;
(iv) if $a, b \in P$, then $a + b \in P$;
(v) if $a \in P$ and $b \in G$, then $-b + a + b \in P$.
The set P is the *positive cone* of $(G, +, \leqslant)$.

5. Let P be a subset of a group $(G, +)$ which has the five properties listed in Exercise 4. Show that there is a total ordering $\leqslant$ on G such that $(G, +, \leqslant)$ is a totally ordered group with positive cone P.

6. Show that a totally ordered group $(G, +, \leqslant:)$ is order-isomorphic to $(\mathbf{Z}, +, \leqslant)$ if and only if the following two conditions hold:
(i) G contains more than one element;
(ii) every non-empty subset of G which is bounded below contains a greatest lower bound.

7. Let $(G, +, \leqslant)$ and $(H, \oplus, \leqslant:)$ be totally ordered groups. A subset K of G is *convex* if, whenever $a, b \in K$, $c \in G$, and $a \leqslant c \leqslant b$, then $c \in K$. An *order-homomorphism* from $(G, +, \leqslant)$ to $(H, \oplus, \leqslant:)$ is a homomorphism f from $(G, +)$ to $(H, \oplus)$ with the property: if $a, b \in G$ and $a \leqslant b$, then $f(a) \leqslant: f(b)$. Show that a subset of G is the kernel of an order-homomorphism from $(G, +, \leqslant)$ if and only if it is a convex normal subgroup of $(G, +, \leqslant)$.

8. From the properties of $\log_a x$ which were stated following Theorem 22, show that:
(i) for all positive real numbers x and all integers r,
$$\log_a x^r = r \log_a x;$$
(ii) for every real number y, there is a unique positive real number a^y such that $y = \log_a a^y$;
(iii) $a^x a^y = a^{x+y}$ and $(a^x)^y = a^{xy}$ for all real numbers x, y.

9. Find necessary and sufficient conditions on a subset of a ring for it to be the positive cone for some total ordering of that ring, and find necessary and sufficient conditions for it to be the kernel for an order-(ring-)homomorphism.

10. Let $(G, +)$ be a commutative group and let A be the set of those elements of G which have non-0 order. By Exercise 8, p. 92, the difference group $(G - A, \oplus)$ exists and its elements have order 0 or 1. If $(G - A, \oplus, \leqslant)$ is a totally ordered group, show that the relation $\leqslant:$ defined on G by '$a \leqslant: b$ if and only if $A + a \leqslant A + b$' has the following properties:
(i) G is quasi-ordered by $\leqslant:$;
(ii) if $a, b, c \in G$ and $a \leqslant: b$, then $a + c \leqslant: b + c$;
(iii) if $a, b \in G$, then $a \leqslant: b$ and $b \leqslant: a$ if and only if $a - b$ has non-0 order.

Show, conversely, that if $\leqslant:$ is a relation on G with the above three properties, then $(G - A, \oplus)$ can be totally ordered by a relation $\leqslant$ defined in the obvious way.

CHAPTER 4

POLYNOMIALS AND RATIONAL FUNCTIONS

1 Polynomials

A 'polynomial' is sometimes defined to be 'an expression of the form

$$a_0 + a_1 x + a_2 x^2 + \ldots + a_n x^n,$$

where n is a positive integer, $a_0, a_1, a_2, \ldots, a_n$ are real numbers or, more generally, elements of a ring or field, and the symbols $+, x, x^2, x^3, \ldots, x^n$ are undefined'. This definition is clearly unacceptable here, since neither the phrase 'an expression of the form' nor the symbols $+, x, x^2, x^3, \ldots, x^n$ are defined; but the intention of the definition is clear. A finite sequence $a_0, a_1, a_2, \ldots, a_n$ of elements from a specified set is to determine a polynomial, which is written

$$a_0 + a_1 x + a_2 x^2 + \ldots + a_n x^n,$$

and then polynomials are to be added and multiplied together in a familiar way. This suggests that we define a polynomial to be a finite sequence and that, for example, $(1, 0, 2)$, $(1, 0, 2, 0)$, and $(1, 0, 2, 0, 0)$ are polynomials which we would write as $1 + 0x + 2x^2$, $1 + 0x + 2x^2 + 0x^3$, and $1 + 0x + 2x^2 + 0x^3 + 0x^4$, respectively. But these polynomials are usually regarded as the same polynomial and are written $1 + 2x^2$. This suggests that a polynomial be defined to be a set of finite sequences or else to be an infinite sequence in which only a finite number of terms are non-zero. The second way is obviously preferable; it is easier to consider one infinite sequence rather than a set of finite sequences.

We will therefore define a polynomial to be a special kind of sequence, the elements of which are taken from a specified set. Since the addition and multiplication of polynomials will involve the addition and multiplication of these elements, they will be taken from a ring.

DEFINITIONS. Let $(G, +, \cdot)$ be a ring. A *polynomial over* $(G, +, \cdot)$ is an infinite sequence of elements from G, only a finite number of terms in the sequence being non-0. The polynomial $a_0, a_1, a_2, \ldots$ is written

$$a_0 + a_1 x + a_2 x^2 + \ldots,$$

where those constituents $a_i x^i$ for which $a_i = 0$ may be omitted.

The element a_i is the *i-th coefficient* of the polynomial. If all the coefficients of a polynomial are 0, then the polynomial is denoted by 0. If a polynomial f is not 0, then there is a largest integer n such that the n-th coefficient of f is not 0. This integer is the *degree* of f, and is denoted by 'deg f'. The (deg f)-th coefficient of f is the *leading coefficient* of f. The set of all polynomials over $(G, +, \cdot)$ is denoted by $G[x]$.

Let

$$f = a_0 + a_1 x + a_2 x^2 + \ldots$$
$$g = b_0 + b_1 x + b_2 x^2 + \ldots$$

be polynomials over $(G, +, \cdot)$. The *sum* $f + g$ and the *product* $f \cdot g$ of f and g are the polynomials whose i-th coefficients are $a_i + b_i$ and $\sum_{s+t=i} a_s \cdot b_t$, respectively, where by $\sum_{s+t=i} a_s \cdot b_t$ is meant the sum of all those terms $a_s \cdot b_t$ for which $s + t = i$. (This is obviously a finite sum and, since $(G, +)$ is a commutative group, the order of the terms in the sum need not be specified.)

Remarks. (i) We have ascribed no meaning to the symbols $+$, x, $x^2, \ldots$ in the definition of polynomial. They are used merely as 'place' symbols, to separate a_0 from a_1, a_1 from a_2, and so on. They could be introduced in a natural way as follows. Suppose that $(G, +, \cdot)$ has an identity I, and denote the polynomial $0, I, 0, 0, \ldots$ by x. Then, writing x^2 for $x \cdot x$, x^3 for $x \cdot x^2$, and so on, and using the definitions of sum and product, we have

$$x^2 = (0, 0, I, 0, 0, \ldots),$$
$$x^3 = (0, 0, 0, I, 0, 0, \ldots),$$

etc., so that the polynomial $a_0, a_1, a_2, \ldots$ can be written

$$a_0 + a_1 \cdot x + a_2 \cdot x^2 + \ldots.$$

This is reminiscent of the way the notation $a + ib$ for the complex number $\langle a, b \rangle$ was developed on p. 56.

If $(G, +, \cdot)$ is a ring with identity I, then by x we will always mean the polynomial Ix, as above.

(ii) It might appear that there would be some confusion between the ring element a and the polynomial $a + 0x + 0x^2 + \ldots$, since they are both denoted by the same symbol a. Consider the function f from G to $G[x]$ defined by

$$f(a) = a + 0x + 0x^2 + \ldots$$

for all $a \in G$. This function is obviously an injection and, for all $a, b \in G$,

$$f(a + b) = (a + b) + 0x + 0x^2$$
$$= (a + 0x + 0x^2 + \ldots) + (b + 0x + 0x^2 + \ldots)$$
$$= f(a) + f(b),$$

and similarly

$$f(a \cdot b) = f(a) \cdot f(b).$$

Thus G can be considered to be embedded in $G[x]$ by f, and no ambiguity will arise if a and $f(a)$ are denoted by a. The elements of G are sometimes referred to as *constant polynomials*.

(iii) If $(G, +, \cdot)$ has an identity, so that the polynomial x exists, then, for all $a \in G$,

$$\begin{aligned} x \cdot a &= (0 + Ix + 0x^2 + \ldots) \cdot (a + 0x + 0x^2 + \ldots) \\ &= 0 + (0 + I \cdot a)x + 0x^2 + \ldots \\ &= a \cdot x. \end{aligned}$$

DEFINITION. Two polynomials f, g over a ring *commute* if $f \cdot g = g \cdot f$.

We have just shown that x commutes with every element of G and thus, since x obviously commutes with x^2, x^3, x^4,..., it commutes with all the polynomials in $G[x]$.

(iv) The assertion that every non-0 polynomial has a degree involves the well-ordering of the integers: if $f = a_0 + a_1 x + a_2 x^2 + \ldots$ is a non-0 polynomial, then the set $\{i \mid i \in \mathbf{Z}$ and $a_j = 0$ for all $j > i\}$ is not empty, by the definition of the term 'polynomial', and hence has a least member, which is $\deg f$.

We will see that the purely algebraic properties of polynomials – as distinct from those properties which are a consequence of the connection between polynomials and functions – are similar to the properties of the integers. This similarity is founded on two facts. First, the set of polynomials over an integral domain is an integral domain. Secondly, if A is a set of polynomials and A contains a non-0 polynomial, then A contains a polynomial of least degree. That is, $(\mathbf{Z}, +, \cdot)$ and $(G[x], +, \cdot)$ have the same algebraic structure if G is an integral domain, and they have similar order properties. Of course, a set of polynomials may contain two different polynomials of least degree, and this introduces a lack of uniqueness into some of the results.

THEOREM 1. *If* $(G, +, \cdot)$ *is a ring, then* $(G[x], +, \cdot)$ *is a ring. If* $(G, +, \cdot)$ *is an integral domain, then* $(G[x], +, \cdot)$ *is an integral domain.*

Proof. $(G[x], +)$ is clearly a commutative group. If one of the polynomials f, g is 0, then $f \cdot g = 0$. If neither f nor g is 0, then the i-th coefficient of $f \cdot g$ is 0 if $i > \deg f + \deg g$. Thus the product of two polynomials is a polynomial.

To show that the multiplication of polynomials is associative, let f, g, h

be polynomials in $G[x]$ whose i-th coefficients are a_i, b_i, c_i respectively. Then the i-th coefficient of $(f \cdot g) \cdot h$ is

$$\sum_{s+t=i} \left(\sum_{n+m=s} a_n \cdot b_m \right) \cdot c_t.$$

This is a sum of terms of the type $a_n \cdot b_m \cdot c_t$ where $n + m + t = i$. On the other hand, if n, m, t are non-negative integers such that $n + m + t = i$, then there is clearly a corresponding term $a_n \cdot b_m \cdot c_t$ in this sum, and so the i-th coefficient of $(f \cdot g) \cdot h$ is the sum of all terms of the type $a_n \cdot b_m \cdot c_t$, where $n + m + t = i$. Similarly, this sum is also the i-th coefficient of $f \cdot (g \cdot h)$, and so $(f \cdot g) \cdot h = f \cdot (g \cdot h)$.

The distributive law for $G[x]$ follows easily from the distributive law for G, and so $(G[x], +, \cdot)$ is a ring.

If $(G, +, \cdot)$ is an integral domain, then the commutativity of the ring $(G[x], +, \cdot)$ follows easily from the commutativity of $(G, +, \cdot)$, and the multiplicative identity in G is the identity in $G[x]$. If a and b are the leading coefficients of non-0 polynomials f and g, then $a \cdot b$ is the leading coefficient of $f \cdot g$; and since $a \neq 0$, $b \neq 0$, and a, b are in an integral domain, $a \cdot b \neq 0$. Thus $f \cdot g \neq 0$. $\square$

By the first and last parts of the above proof, we have:

(i) *if f, g are non-0 polynomials over a ring, then either $f \cdot g = 0$ or* $\deg f \cdot g \leqslant \deg f + \deg g$;

(ii) *if f, g are non-0 polynomials over an integral domain, then* $\deg f \cdot g = \deg f + \deg g$.

We will denote the largest member of a finite set of real numbers a, b, $c, \ldots$, by $\max(a, b, c, \ldots)$. It should be clear from the definition of the sum of two polynomials that:

(iii) *if f, g are non-0 polynomials over a ring, then either $f + g = 0$ or else* $\deg(f + g) \leqslant \max(\deg f, \deg g)$.

These conditions on the degrees of $f + g$ and $f \cdot g$ are most important and will be frequently used in the proofs that follow. In some of these proofs the polynomial 0 must be treated separately, and the statements of the theorems make special reference to it. This is usually because the proofs use the well-ordering of the degrees, and 0 has no degree. It might appear that these difficulties could be avoided if $\deg 0$ were defined in such a way that

$$\deg f \cdot g \leqslant \deg f + \deg g$$

and

$$\deg(f + g) \leqslant \max(\deg f, \deg g)$$

for all polynomials f, g over a ring. If this were done, then, from the first condition,

$$\deg 0 \leqslant \deg 0 + \deg 0$$

so that $\deg 0 \geqslant 0$, and from the second condition,

$$\deg 0 = \deg(1-1) \leqslant 0.$$

Thus, if $\deg 0$ is to be defined in such a way as to satisfy these conditions, then it must be defined to be 0. This would be a satisfactory definition if we were only going to consider polynomials over rings, but the stronger condition

$$\deg f \cdot g = \deg f + \deg g$$

which holds for non-0 polynomials over an integral domain no longer holds if $\deg 0$ is defined to be 0, since it would imply that

$$0 = \deg 0 \cdot f = \deg 0 + \deg f = \deg f$$

for all polynomials f. There is one other possibility. If we extended the real number system to include the infinite real numbers ∞ and $-\infty$, then $\deg 0$ could satisfactorily be defined to be $-\infty$. We will not do this, as the small advantage is not worth the difficulty. To do it would only simplify the statements of some theorems and obscure some difficulties in their proofs.

THEOREM 2 (*The Division Theorem*). *If f, g are polynomials over a field $(G, +, \cdot)$ and $g \neq 0$, then there are unique polynomials q, r over $(G, +, \cdot)$ such that $f = g \cdot q + r$ and either $r = 0$ or $\deg r < \deg g$.*[1]

Proof. The proof is similar to that of Theorem 14, Chapter 1. We show first that there are polynomials q, r over G satisfying the conditions, and then that they are unique.

Let

$$A = \{s \,|\, s \in G[x] \text{ and } s = f - g \cdot h \text{ for some } h \in G[x]\}.$$

If $0 \in A$, so that $0 = f - g \cdot h$ for some $h \in G[x]$, let $q = h$ and let $r = 0$. Obviously, q and r satisfy the required conditions.

Suppose that $0 \notin A$. Since A is not empty, it contains a polynomial r of least degree. Let q be the polynomial such that $r = f - g \cdot q$. We now show that $\deg r < \deg g$.

Suppose that this is not the case, that is, that $\deg r \geqslant \deg g$. Then either

$$\deg (r - (a/b) \cdot g \cdot x^m) < \deg r$$

---

[1] q is called the *quotient* and r the *remainder* obtained when g is divided into f.

or $r - (a/b) \cdot g \cdot x^m = 0$, where a is the leading coefficient of r, b is the leading coefficient of g, and $m = \deg r - \deg g$. But

$$r - (a/b) \cdot g \cdot x^m = f - g \cdot q - (a/b) \cdot g \cdot x^m$$
$$= f - g \cdot (q + (a/b) \cdot x^m),$$

and so $r - (a/b) \cdot g \cdot x^m$ is in A and yet has degree less than that of r, or is 0. This contradicts either our choice of r or our assumption that $0 \notin A$. Thus, $\deg r < \deg g$.

Now we must show that q and r are uniquely determined by f and g. Suppose that

$$f = g \cdot q + r = g \cdot q' + r',$$

where q, q', r, r', are polynomials such that either $r = 0$ or $\deg r < \deg g$, and either $r' = 0$ or $\deg r' < \deg g$. We have

$$r - r' = g \cdot (q' - q).$$

If $q' - q \neq 0$, then $\deg g \cdot (q' - q) \geqslant \deg g$. But $\deg r - r' < \deg g$ or $r - r' = 0$. Thus $q' - q = 0$, and so $r - r' = 0$. □

Theorem 2 does not hold if 'field' is replaced by 'integral domain'. For example, there are no polynomials q, r over the integral domain $(\mathbf{Z}, +, \cdot)$ such that $x = (2x) \cdot q + r$ and either $r = 0$ or $\deg r < \deg 2x$. By the conditions on their degrees, both q and r would have to be integers and so $1 = 2q$ – which is impossible – and $r = 0$. Of course, a polynomial over $(\mathbf{Z}, +, \cdot)$ is also a polynomial over the field of rational numbers. In general, a polynomial over an integral domain is also a polynomial over a field, since an integral domain can be embedded in a field, by Theorem 19, p. 96, and so Theorem 2 can be generalized to polynomials over integral domains as follows:

If f, g are polynomials over an integral domain and $g \neq 0$, then there are unique polynomials q, r over a field containing this integral domain, such that $f = g \cdot q + r$ and either $r = 0$ or $\deg r < \deg g$.

Furthermore, from the property of the field constructed in the proof of Theorem 19, there is a non-0 element c in the integral domain such that cq and cr are polynomials over the integral domain.

DEFINITIONS. Let f and g be polynomials over a field $(G, +, \cdot)$. If there is a polynomial q over $(G, +, \cdot)$ such that $f = g \cdot q$, then g *divides* f, or is a *divisor* of f, and this is denoted by $g \,|\, f$. If the leading coefficient of f is the multiplicative identity of the field, then f is *monic*. The *greatest common divisor* of f and g, denoted by (f, g), is a monic polynomial which is a common divisor of f and g of largest degree.

That is, h is the greatest common divisor of f and g if h is monic, $h \mid f$ and $h \mid g$, and, whenever deg $k >$ deg h, then k fails to divide at least one of f and g.

If f and g are polynomials over a field then they have common divisors, since every polynomial of degree 0 divides every polynomial. If $f \neq 0$ and $h \mid f$, then deg $h \leqslant$ deg f. Thus, if at least one of f, g is not 0, then the set of degrees of all possible common divisors of f and g is not empty and is bounded above, and so f and g have a common divisor of largest degree. Let h be such a common divisor. Since $h \neq 0$, it has a leading coefficient a, and it is easy to see that $a^{-1} \cdot h$ is the greatest common divisor of f and g. We have thus shown that, if f and g are polynomials over a field and at least one of f and g is not 0, then they have a greatest common divisor.

We now show that, if $f \neq 0$, then (f, g) is uniquely determined by f and g. We proceed by induction. If deg $f = 0$, then (f, g) must be the multiplicative identity of the field. Suppose that (f, g) is uniquely determined by f and g for all polynomials f, g such that deg $f \leqslant n$, and let f be a polynomial of degree $n + 1$. By the division theorem, there are polynomials q, r such that $g = f \cdot q + r$ and either $r = 0$ or deg $r <$ deg f. Clearly, every common divisor of f and g is a common divisor of f and r and conversely, and so f and g have the same greatest common divisors as f and r. If $r = 0$ then (f, r) must be $a^{-1} \cdot f$, where a is the leading coefficient of f. If $r \neq 0$ then (f, r) is unique, since deg $r < n$. This proves the required result, by the principle of induction.

We have now shown that if f and g are polynomials over a field G, and $f \neq 0$, then (f, g) exists and is unique. Suppose that f and g are polynomials over a subfield H of G. Then f and g have a greatest common divisor (f, g) with respect to G, and a greatest common divisor h, with respect to H. We now show that $h = (f, g)$. The proof is by induction. If deg $f = 0$, then h is the multiplicative identity of H and (f, g) is the multiplicative identity of G, and so, because these identities are equal (p. 71), $h = (f, g)$. Suppose that the greatest common divisor of f and g with respect to H is the greatest common divisor of f and g with respect to G, for all polynomials f and g over H such that deg $f \leqslant n$. Let f and g be polynomials over H such that deg $f = n + 1$ and let q, r be polynomials over H such that $g = f \cdot q + r$ and either $r = 0$ or deg $r <$ deg f. If $r = 0$ then (f, g) must be $a^{-1} \cdot f$, where a is the leading coefficient of f. If $r \neq 0$ then the greatest common divisor of f and r with respect to H (which is the greatest common divisor of f and g with respect to H) is, by our assumption, the greatest common divisor of f and r with respect to G and this is the greatest common divisor of f and g with respect to G. By the principle of induction, this completes the proof, and we have now shown that:

If f and g are polynomials over a subfield H of a field G, and $f \neq 0$, then the greatest common divisor of f and g with respect to H is the greatest common divisor of f and g with respect to G.

This is rather a surprising result. It might be thought that there could be a common divisor of f and g in $G[x]$ which has a larger degree than that of any common divisor of f and g in $H[x]$, since there may be common divisors of f and g in $G[x]$ which are not in $H[x]$.

EXAMPLE. Consider the polynomials

$$f = (x^2 - 2) \cdot (x - 1),$$
$$g = (x^2 - 2) \cdot (x + 1).$$

Their monic common divisors over $\mathbf{Q}$ are 1 and $x^2 - 2$, and over $\mathbf{R}$ are 1, $x^2 - 2$, $x - \sqrt{2}$, and $x + \sqrt{2}$. The monic common divisor of largest degree is the same in both cases; it is $x^2 - 2$.

The greatest common divisor of two polynomials can be found by using the division theorem as in Euclid's algorithm, p. 25.

EXAMPLE. Suppose that we wish to find the greatest common divisor of

$$f = x^3 - 2x^2 + x - 2$$

and $$g = x^4 - 2x^3 - x + 2.$$

First we divide f into g to obtain

$$g = f \cdot x + (-x^2 + x + 2).$$

Then $-x^2 + x + 2$ is divided into f to obtain

$$f = (-x^2 + x + 2) \cdot (-x + 1) + (2x - 4),$$

and then $2x - 4$ is divided into $-x^2 + x + 2$ to obtain

$$-x^2 + x + 2 = (2x - 4) \cdot (-\tfrac{1}{2}x - \tfrac{1}{2}).$$

The last non-0 remainder is $2x - 4$, which is therefore a common divisor of highest degree. Thus, $(f, g) = x - 2$.

The proof of the next theorem is similar to that of Theorem 15, p. 25.

THEOREM 3. *If f and g are polynomials over a field $(G, +, \cdot)$, and at least one of f, g is not 0, then:*
(i) *there are polynomials $s, t \in G[x]$ such that $(f, g) = s \cdot f + t \cdot g$;*
(ii) *if $c \mid f$ and $c \mid g$, then $c \mid (f, g)$.*

DEFINITIONS. Two polynomials f, g over a field $(G, +, \cdot)$ are *relatively prime* if at least one of them is not 0 and $(f, g) = I$. A polynomial f is *prime over a field* $(G, +, \cdot)$ if f is a polynomial in $G[x]$ whose only divisors in $G[x]$ have degree 0 or degree $\deg f$.

If two polynomials over a field G are relatively prime, and G is embedded in a larger field, then, because their greatest common divisor with respect to G is the same as their greatest common divisor with respect to the larger field, they are relatively prime with respect to the larger field. Thus polynomials need not be described as being 'relatively prime with respect to a field'. However, the property of being prime does depend on the field, as the following examples show.

EXAMPLES. (i) $x^2 - 2$ is prime over $(\mathbf{Q}, +, \cdot)$ because, if $x^2 - 2 = (x - a) \cdot (x - b)$ where a, b are rational numbers, then, multiplying out the right-hand side and equating coefficients, we would have $a^2 = b^2 = 2$, and there are no rational numbers for which this holds. Since $x^2 - 2 = (x - \sqrt{2}) \cdot (x + \sqrt{2})$, $x^2 - 2$ is not prime over $(\mathbf{R}, +, \cdot)$.

(ii) Similarly, $x^2 + 1$ is prime over $(\mathbf{R}, +, \cdot)$ but not prime over $(\mathbf{C}, +, \cdot)$.

The polynomial 0 is certainly not prime over any field – every polynomial divides it. Suppose that f and g are polynomials over a field G and that f is prime over G. Then (f, g) exists, because $f \neq 0$, and $\deg (f, g)$ is either 0 or $\deg f$. If $\deg (f, g) = 0$, then f and g are relatively prime. If $\deg (f, g) = \deg f$, then $f = a \cdot (f, g)$, where a is the leading coefficient of f, and so $f \mid g$. Thus, *a prime polynomial either divides a given polynomial or is relatively prime to it.*

The proof of the next theorem is similar to the proofs of Theorems 16 and 17, p. 27.

THEOREM 4. *Let* $f, g_1, g_2, g_3, \ldots, g_n$ *be polynomials over a field* $(G, +, \cdot)$. *Then:*

(i) f *and* g_1 *are relatively prime if and only if there are polynomials* $s, t \in G[x]$ *such that*

$$I = s \cdot f + t \cdot g;$$

(ii) *if* f *and* g_1 *are relatively prime and* $f \mid g_1 \cdot g_2$, *then* $f \mid g_2$;

(iii) *if* f *is prime over* $(G, +, \cdot)$ *and* $f \mid g_1 \cdot g_2 \cdot g_3 \cdot \ldots \cdot g_n$, *then* $f \mid g_i$ *for some* i.

THEOREM 5 (*The Unique Factorization Theorem for Polynomials*). *If* f *is a polynomial over a field* $(G, +, \cdot)$, *and* $\deg f > 0$, *then there are polynomials* $g_1, g_2, g_3, \ldots, g_n$ *which are monic, prime over* G, *and of degree* > 0, *and an element* $c \in G$, *such that*

$$f = c \cdot g_1 \cdot g_2 \cdot g_3 \cdot \ldots \cdot g_n.$$

The polynomials $g_1, g_2, g_3, \ldots, g_n$ *are uniquely determined by* f, *apart from order, and* c *is uniquely determined by* f.

Proof. The proof is similar to that of Theorem 18, p. 28. First we show that every polynomial of positive degree can be factorized in the required way. If this is not the case, then there is a polynomial f of least degree which cannot be so factorized. Every prime polynomial can obviously be expressed in the required way, so f is not prime. Thus there are polynomials g, $h \in G[x]$ such that $f = g \cdot h$ and with degrees less than $\deg f$. Since f is a product of polynomials which can be factorized, f can also be factorized. This is a contradiction, and proves that every polynomial of positive degree can be factorized as required.

Now we will show that the factorization of f is unique. Certainly, c is uniquely determined by f, since it is the leading coefficient of f. Thus we need only show that, if g_1, g_2, g_3, ..., g_n are monic, prime, and of positive degree, then $g_1 \cdot g_2 \cdot g_3 \cdot ... \cdot g_n$ uniquely determines g_1, g_2, g_3, ..., g_n, apart from order. We will prove this by induction on n.

If $g_1 = h_1 \cdot h_2 \cdot h_3 \cdot ... \cdot h_r$, where h_1, h_2, h_3, ..., h_r are monic, prime, and of positive degree, then $r = 1$ and $g_1 = h_1$, since g_1 is prime.

Now suppose that $g_1 \cdot g_2 \cdot g_3 \cdot ... \cdot g_{n-1}$ uniquely determines g_1, g_2, g_3, ..., g_{n-1} and that $g_1 \cdot g_2 \cdot g_3 \cdot ... \cdot g_n = h_1 \cdot h_2 \cdot h_3 \cdot ... \cdot h_r$, where h_1, h_2, h_3, ..., h_r are monic, prime, and of positive degree. By Theorem 4(iii), $g_n | h_i$ for some i. Since g_n and h_i are both monic, prime, and of positive degree, $g_n = h_i$. Thus,

$$g_1 \cdot g_2 \cdot g_3 \cdot ... \cdot g_{n-1} = h_1 \cdot h_2 \cdot h_3 \cdot ... \cdot h_{i-1} \cdot h_{i+1} \cdot ... \cdot h_r$$

and so, by our assumption, $g_1, g_2, g_3, ..., g_{n-1}$ and $h_1, h_2, h_3, ..., h_{i-1}, h_{i+1}, ...,$ h_r are the same, apart from order. Since $g_n = h_i$ this proves the required result. □

The term 'prime' was defined to apply only to polynomials over fields, but it can obviously be extended to polynomials over commutative rings, and the term 'monic' can be extended to polynomials over rings with identity. It is interesting to note that if this is done, then Theorems 4 and 5 no longer hold if 'field' is replaced by 'commutative ring with identity'. For example, the polynomial

$$x^2 + [2]x + [1]$$

over the ring of residue classes modulo 4 can be factorized in two ways:

$$x^2 + [2]x + [1] = (x - [1])^2 = (x - [3])^2.$$

An examination of the proof of Theorem 5 shows that a polynomial of positive degree over a commutative ring is the product of 'prime' polynomials but, as the above example shows, the factorization need not be unique. Nor can the factors necessarily be chosen to be monic, even if the ring has an identity; $[2]x + [1]$, over the above ring, is not the product of a ring element and a monic polynomial.

EXERCISES

1. Find the greatest common divisors of the following pairs of polynomials, and express them as appropriate linear combinations:
(i) $x^4 + x^3 - 6x^2 - 4x + 8$, $x^3 + 2x^2 - x - 2$, over $(\mathbf{Q}, +, \cdot)$;
(ii) $x^3 + [4]x$, $x^4 + [4]$, over the field of residue classes modulo 5;
(iii) $x^2 + 1$, $2x^3 + 3ix^2 - x$, over $(\mathbf{C}, +, \cdot)$.

2. Find those values of a such that the greatest common divisor of
$$x^2 + (2 - a)x - 2a \text{ and } x^3 + ax^2 - x - a$$
is of degree 1.

3. List the monic polynomials of degree 2 over the field of residue classes modulo 3, and express each of them as a product of monic prime polynomials.

4. Prove that, if f and g are polynomials over a field, and $f^2 \mid g^2$, then $f \mid g$.

5. Prove that, if f and g are polynomials over $(\mathbf{Q}, +, \cdot)$ and are relatively prime, then $f + g$ and $f - g$ are relatively prime.
Prove that, if p is a prime integer, $p \neq \pm 1$, and f and g are relatively prime polynomials over the field of residue classes modulo p, then $f + g$ and $f - g$ are relatively prime if $p \neq \pm 2$, but need not be relatively prime if $p = \pm 2$.

6. Let f and g be non-0 polynomials over a field, and let k be a positive integer. Prove that $\deg(f, g) \geqslant k$ if and only if there are polynomials a, b such that $a \cdot f = b \cdot g$, $\deg a \leqslant \deg g - k$, and $\deg b \leqslant \deg f - k$.

7. Let h be a polynomial with positive degree over a field G, and let K be the set of all those polynomials over G with degree less than $\deg h$ and the polynomial 0. For $f, g \in K$, let $f \times g$ be the remainder obtained when $f \cdot g$ is divided by h. Show that $(K, +, \times)$, where $+$ is the usual operation of addition, is a ring, and that it is a field if and only if h is prime over G.

2   Polynomial functions

If
$$f = a_0 + a_1 x + a_2 x^2 + \ldots + a_n x^n$$
is a polynomial over a ring G, and $b \in G$, then
$$a_0 + a_1 \cdot b + a_2 \cdot b^2 + \ldots + a_n \cdot b^n$$
is an element of G. It will be denoted by $f(b)$. In this way the polynomial f is associated with a function from G to G. This function will also be denoted by f, the same symbol that is used for the polynomial, and it should be clear from the context whether f refers to a polynomial or to a function. The distinction is sometimes important. For example, if G is a field which

contains only a finite number of elements, say b_1, b_2, b_3,..., b_n, then the polynomial

$$f = (x - b_1) \cdot (x - b_2) \cdot (x - b_3) \cdot \ldots \cdot (x - b_n)$$

is clearly not 0, since it has degree n, but the associated function is 0. That is, $f(b) = 0$ for all $b \in G$. Since the polynomial 0 is also associated with the function 0, we see that different polynomials may be associated with the same function.

DEFINITION. A function f from a ring G to G is a *polynomial function* if there is a polynomial

$$a_0 + a_1 x + a_2 x^2 + \ldots + a_n x^n$$

over G such that

$$f(b) = a_0 + a_1 \cdot b + a_2 \cdot b^2 + \ldots + a_n \cdot b^n$$

for all $b \in G$.

In Example (vi), p. 94, we proved that the set K of all functions from a set A to a ring G is a ring under the operations $+$ and $\cdot$ defined by

$$(f + g)(x) = f(x) + g(x)$$
and
$$(f \cdot g)(x) = f(x) \cdot g(x).$$

The set of all polynomial functions from a ring G to G is obviously a subset of the set of all functions from G to G. We now show that, if G is a commutative ring, then the set of polynomial functions from G to G is a homomorphic image of $G[x]$, and so is a subring of the ring of all functions from G to G.

THEOREM 6. *Let $(G, +, \cdot)$ be a commutative ring, let $(K, +, \cdot)$ be the ring of all functions from G to G, and let α be the function from $G[x]$ to K which associates with the polynomial*

$$f = a_0 + a_1 x + a_2 x^2 + \ldots + a_n x^n$$

the function $\alpha(f)$ defined by

$$\alpha(f)(b) = a_0 + a_1 \cdot b + a_2 \cdot b^2 + \ldots + a_n \cdot b^n.$$

Then α is a homomorphism from $(G[x], +, \cdot)$ to $(K, +, \cdot)$.

Proof. We must show that $\alpha(f + g) = \alpha(f) + \alpha(g)$ and $\alpha(f \cdot g) = \alpha(f) \cdot \alpha(g)$ for all $f, g \in G[x]$. Let

$$f = a_0 + a_1 x + a_2 x^2 + \ldots$$
and
$$g = b_0 + b_1 x + b_2 x^2 + \ldots$$

be polynomials in $G[x]$. We must show that

$$(a_0 + b_0) + (a_1 + b_1) \cdot b + (a_2 + b_2) \cdot b^2 + \ldots$$
$$= (a_0 + a_1 \cdot b + a_2 \cdot b^2 + \ldots) + (b_0 + b_1 \cdot b + b_2 \cdot b^2 + \ldots)$$

and that

$$(a_0 \cdot b_0) + (a_0 \cdot b_1 + a_1 \cdot b_0) \cdot b + (a_0 \cdot b_2 + a_1 \cdot b_1 + a_2 \cdot b_0) \cdot b^2 + \ldots$$
$$= (a_0 + a_1 \cdot b + a_2 \cdot b^2 + \ldots) \cdot (b_0 + b_1 \cdot b + b_2 \cdot b^2 + \ldots)$$

for all $b \in G$. These equalities clearly hold if $f = 0$ or if $\deg f = 0$, and can be shown to hold in general by induction on the degree of f. The details are left to the reader. □

DEFINITIONS. Let f be a polynomial over a field $(G, +, \cdot)$, and let n be a positive integer. An element $a \in G$ is a *root of multiplicity n of f* if f is divisible by $(x - a)^n$ but not divisible by $(x - a)^{n+1}$. If a is a root of multiplicity n of f for some n, then it is a *root* of f. If a is a root of multiplicity n of f for some $n > 1$, then it is a *multiple root* of f.

THEOREM 7. *Let f be a polynomial over a field. Then*:
(i) *if a is a root of f, then $f(a) = 0$;*
(ii) *if $f \neq 0$ and $f(a) = 0$, then a is a root of f;*
(iii) *if $a_1, a_2, a_3, \ldots, a_r$ are different roots of f of multiplicities $m_1, m_2, m_3, \ldots, m_r$, respectively, then $(x - a_1)^{m_1} \cdot (x - a_2)^{m_2} \cdot (x - a_3)^{m_3} \cdot \ldots \cdot (x - a_r)^{m_r} | f$.*

Proof. (i) If a is a root of f, then there is an integer $n > 0$ and a polynomial h such that $f = (x - a)^n \cdot h$. By Theorem 6, $f(b) = (b - a)^n \cdot h(b)$ for all b in the field, and so $f(a) = (a - a)^n \cdot h(a) = 0$;

(ii) By the division theorem, there are polynomials q, r such that $f = q \cdot (x - a) + r$ and either $r = 0$ or $\deg r < 1$. By Theorem 6,

$$0 = f(a) = q(a) \cdot 0 + r(a),$$

so that $r(a) = 0$. Since r is a constant polynomial, $r = 0$. Thus $(x - a) | f$. Therefore, the set $\{n \mid n$ is a positive integer and $(x - a)^n | f\}$ is not empty. It is bounded above by $\deg f$, and so contains a largest member m. Clearly, a is a root of multiplicity m of f.

(iii) We proceed by induction on r. If $r = 1$, the result follows immediately from the definition of 'root of multiplicity n'. Suppose that there is a polynomial h such that

$$f = (x - a_1)^{m_1} \cdot (x - a_2)^{m_2} \cdot (x - a_3)^{m_3} \cdot \ldots \cdot (x - a_{r-1})^{m_{r-1}} \cdot h.$$

The polynomials $(x - a_1)^{m_1} \cdot (x - a_2)^{m_2} \cdot (x - a_3)^{m_3} \cdot \ldots \cdot (x - a_{r-1})^{m_{r-1}}$ and $(x - a_r)^{m_r}$ are relatively prime, and so, by Theorem 4(ii), $(x - a_r)^{m_r} | h$. Thus

$$(x - a_1)^{m_1} \cdot (x - a_2)^{m_2} \cdot (x - a_3)^{m_3} \cdot \ldots \cdot (x - a_r)^{m_r} | f. \quad \square$$

In the proof of (i) of the above theorem, we used no properties of the field except the commutativity of multiplication (in order to apply Theorem 6) and the existence of a multiplicative identity. Thus, part (i) can be generalized to polynomials over commutative rings with identity. Part (ii) can also be generalized to such polynomials, and the proof of this is set as Exercise 3.

EXAMPLES. (i) The polynomial $f = x^2 + [1]$, over the field of residue classes modulo 3, has no roots:

$$f([0]) = [0]^2 + [1] = [1];$$
$$f([1]) = [1]^2 + [1] = [2];$$
$$f([2]) = [2]^2 + [1] = [2].$$

(ii) Let G be a non-commutative ring with identity, let a, b be elements of G such that $a \cdot b \neq b \cdot a$, and let $f = (x - a) \cdot (x - b)$. Then $f = x^2 - (a + b)x + a \cdot b$, so that $f(a) = a \cdot b - b \cdot a \neq 0$. Here, f is a (left-) multiple of $x - a$, but $f(a) \neq 0$.

(iii) Let $(G, +)$ be a commutative group, and define the product of any two elements of G to be 0. Then G is a ring. Now let $f = ax$, for some $a \in G$. Then $f(b) = 0$ for all $b \in G$.

THEOREM 8. *Let $(G, +, \cdot)$ be a field which contains an infinite number of elements. Then the ring of polynomials over G is isomorphic to the ring of polynomial functions from G to G.*

Proof. We need only show that the function α of Theorem 6 is an injection. Suppose that f, $g \in G[x]$, and that $f(x) = g(x)$ for all $x \in G$. If $f - g \neq 0$, then, by Theorem 7(ii), every element of G is a root of $f - g$. By Theorem 7(iii), $f - g$ cannot have more than deg $(f - g)$ roots, and so this is a contradiction. □

We now see why, in elementary algebra and analysis, no distinction need be made between a polynomial and the associated polynomial function – the fields considered are usually subfields of the field of complex numbers, and hence contain an infinite number of elements.

DEFINITIONS. Let

$$f = a_0 + a_1 x + a_2 x^2 + \ldots + a_n x^n$$

be a polynomial over a field. The *derivative* of f, denoted by $f^{(1)}$, is the polynomial

$$a_1 + 2a_2 x + 3a_3 x^2 + \ldots + na_n x^{n-1}.$$

The *n-th derivative* of f, denoted by $f^{(n)}$, is defined inductively for all positive integers n by

$$f^{(n)} = (f^{(n-1)})^{(1)}.$$

The derivatives of polynomials over $(\mathbf{R}, +, \cdot)$ and the derivatives of more general real-valued functions of a real variable are studied in every

9

elementary analysis course, and their properties are undoubtedly familiar to the reader. Here the derivative of a polynomial had to be defined without the use of a limiting procedure because, first, there is a distinction between a polynomial and the associated polynomial function and, secondly, the polynomials need not be over fields for which the concept of limit can be reasonably defined. For example, how could 'lim$_{x \to [1]}$ x' be defined if x were confined to the field of residue classes modulo 3 ? It is clear that the usual analytic definition of derivative and our definition give the same results if applied to polynomials over $(\mathbf{R}, +, \cdot)$. Also, the same algebraic laws apply: if f and g are polynomials over a field, then:

(i) $(f+g)^{(1)} = f^{(1)} + g^{(1)}$;

(ii) $(f \cdot g)^{(1)} = f \cdot g^{(1)} + f^{(1)} \cdot g$;

(iii) $(f^n)^{(1)} = nf^{n-1} \cdot f^{(1)}$.

The proof of these results is easy but tedious, and is left to the reader.

THEOREM 9. *If f is a polynomial over $(\mathbf{C}, +, \cdot)$, and a is a root of multiplicity n of f, where $n > 1$, then a is a root of multiplicity $n - 1$ of $f^{(1)}$.*

Proof. We have

$$f = (x - a)^n \cdot g,$$

where $g(a) \neq 0$. Differentiating this,

$$\begin{aligned} f^{(1)} &= n(x - a)^{n-1} \cdot g + (x - a)^n \cdot g^{(1)} \\ &= (x - a)^{n-1} \cdot (ng + (x - a) \cdot g^{(1)}). \end{aligned}$$

The polynomial $ng + (x - a) \cdot g^{(1)}$ has the value $ng(a)$ at a. This is not 0, and so $(x - a)$ does not divide $ng + (x - a) \cdot g^{(1)}$. Thus $(x - a)^n$ does not divide $f^{(1)}$. □

This result is slightly weakened if f is over an arbitrary field – the polynomial $ng + (x - a) \cdot g^{(1)}$ obtained in the proof may be 0 or may have a for a root. Thus:

If f is a polynomial over a field, and a is a root of multiplicity n of f, where $n > 1$, then either a is a root of multiplicity at least $n - 1$ of $f^{(1)}$, or $f^{(1)} = 0$.

EXAMPLES. (i) The polynomial x^3, over the field of residue classes modulo 3, has one root, $[0]$, which is of multiplicity 3. The derivative of x^3 is $[0]$.

(ii) The polynomial $(x - [1])^3 \cdot ((x - [1])^4 + [1])$, over the field of residue classes modulo 3, has a root $[1]$ of multiplicity 3, and $[1]$ is a root of multiplicity 6 of its derivative.

EXERCISES

1. Find all the roots of the following polynomials:
(i) $[2]x^2 - [3]$, over the field of residue classes modulo 5;
(ii) $x^2 - [2]$, over the field of residue classes modulo 3.

2. Show that, if f and g are polynomials over a field, of degrees not exceeding n, and $f(a) = g(a)$ for more than n different elements of the field, then $f = g$.

3. Let G be a commutative ring with identity, let $f \in G[x]$, and let $a \in G$. Show that there is a unique polynomial $q \in G[x]$, such that $f = (x - a) \cdot q + f(a)$. (This result is sometimes called the *Remainder Theorem*.)

4. Show that, if f and g are polynomials over a field G, f is prime over G, and f and g have a common root, then $f \mid g$.

5. Show that a is a root of multiplicity n of a polynomial f over $\mathbf{C}$ if and only if

$$f(a) = f^{(1)}(a) = f^{(2)}(a) = \ldots = f^{(n-1)}(a) = 0$$

and $f^{(n)}(a) \neq 0$.

6. Let f be a non-0 polynomial over $\mathbf{C}$. Show that f has no multiple roots if and only if f and $f^{(1)}$ are relatively prime.

7. Show that $\log_a x$, where a is a fixed real number greater than 1, is not a polynomial function.

8. Let f be a polynomial over $\mathbf{R}$. It can be shown that, if a, b are roots of f and $a \neq b$, then there is a root of $f^{(1)}$ between a and b. Assuming this, show that:
(i) if f has $\deg f$ different roots, then $f^{(1)}$ has $\deg f - 1$ different roots;
(ii) $1 + x + (1/2!)x^2 + \ldots + (1/n!)x^n$ has just one real root if n is odd, and no real root if n is even.

3 Polynomials over the field of complex numbers

In this section we assume the Fundamental Theorem of Algebra: *Every non-constant polynomial over $(\mathbf{C}, +, \cdot)$ has a root.*

THEOREM 10. *A polynomial which is prime over* $(\mathbf{C}, +, \cdot)$ *is of degree* 0 *or degree* 1.

Proof. The polynomial 0 is not prime, and so every prime polynomial has a degree. Suppose that $f \in \mathbf{C}[x]$ and that $\deg f \geq 2$. By the fundamental theorem, f has a root a, and so $(x - a) \mid f$. Since $1 = \deg(x - a) < \deg f$, f cannot be prime. □

From this theorem and Theorem 5 (the unique factorization theorem for polynomials) we have the result:

If f is a non-0 polynomial over $(\mathbf{C}, +, \cdot)$, *then there are complex numbers* $c, z_1, z_2, \ldots, z_{\deg f}$ *such that* $f = c \cdot (x - z_1) \cdot (x - z_2) \cdot \ldots \cdot (x - z_{\deg f})$.

Thus a polynomial over $(\mathbf{C}, +, \cdot)$ of degree n has exactly n roots, if each root is counted as often as its multiplicity specifies.

THEOREM 11. *If f is a polynomial over $(\mathbf{R}, +, \cdot)$, and a is a complex root of f of multiplicity n, then $\bar{a}$, the conjugate of a, is also a root of f of multiplicity n.*

Proof. If $g = a_0 + a_1 x + a_2 x^2 + \ldots$ is a polynomial over $\mathbf{C}$, denote the polynomial $\bar{a}_0 + \bar{a}_1 x + \bar{a}_2 x^2 + \ldots$ by $\bar{g}$. It is easy to verify that $(\overline{g+h}) = \bar{g} + \bar{h}$ and $(\overline{g \cdot h}) = \bar{g} \cdot \bar{h}$ for all polynomials $g, h \in \mathbf{C}[x]$.

Now let f be a polynomial with real coefficients, and let a be a complex root of f of multiplicity n. Then there is a polynomial $g \in \mathbf{C}[x]$ such that $g(a) \neq 0$ and $f = (x - a)^n \cdot g$. From the first remarks,

$$f = \bar{f} = (x - \bar{a})^n \cdot \bar{g}.$$

Since $\bar{g}(\bar{a}) = \overline{g(a)} \neq 0$, $\bar{a}$ is a root of multiplicity n of f. □

Now suppose that f is a non-0 polynomial over $(\mathbf{R}, +, \cdot)$. By Theorems 5 and 10, it is of the form

$$f = c \cdot (x - z_1) \cdot (x - z_2) \cdot \ldots \cdot (x - z_{\deg f}),$$

where $z_1, z_2, \ldots, z_{\deg f}$ are complex numbers, and c, since it is the leading coefficient of f, is a real number. Suppose that z_1 is not real and is of multiplicity n. Then, by Theorem 11, the term

$$(x - z_1)^n \cdot (x - \bar{z}_1)^n$$

occurs in the above product and neither z_1 nor $\bar{z}_1$ occur in any other term of this product. We have

$$((x - z_1) \cdot (x - \bar{z}_1))^n = (x^2 - (z_1 + \bar{z}_1)x + z_1 \cdot \bar{z}_1)^n.$$

The numbers $z_1 + \bar{z}_1$ and $z_1 \cdot \bar{z}_1$ are real. Since this can be done for every non-real root of f, we have the result:

Every polynomial over $(\mathbf{R}, +, \cdot)$ is the product of a real number and monic polynomials over $(\mathbf{R}, +, \cdot)$ of degree 1 or degree 2.

4   Rational functions and partial fractions

We have shown that the set of all polynomials over an integral domain is an integral domain and (in Theorem 19 of Chapter 3) that an integral domain can be embedded in a field. Thus the set of all polynomials over an integral domain can be embedded in a field. The proof of Theorem 19, which was suggested by the way in which the integers were extended to the rational numbers in Chapter 2, shows how a suitable field can be constructed. Let G be an integral domain. If G contains only one element, then

$G[x]$ contains only the polynomial 0 and can obviously be embedded in any field. If G contains at least two elements, let $A = \{\langle a, b \rangle \,|\, a, b \in G[x]$ and $b \neq 0\}$, and let F be the set of equivalence classes defined by the relation α which is defined on A by '$\langle a, b \rangle \,\alpha\, \langle d, e \rangle$ if and only if $a \cdot e = b \cdot d$'. Then F is a field under the operations

$$[\langle a, b \rangle] + [\langle d, e \rangle] = [\langle a \cdot e + b \cdot d, b \cdot e \rangle],$$
$$[\langle a, b \rangle] \cdot [\langle d, e \rangle] = [\langle a \cdot d, b \cdot e \rangle],$$

and since $0 \neq I$, because G contains at least two elements, the function defined by

$$f(a) = [\langle a, I \rangle]$$

is an injective homomorphism, which embeds $G[x]$ in F.

DEFINITIONS. A *rational function over an integral domain* $(G, +, \cdot)$ is an equivalence class determined by the relation α on the set $\{\langle a, b \rangle \,|\, a, b \in G[x]$ and $b \neq 0\}$ defined by '$\langle a, b \rangle \,\alpha\, \langle c, d \rangle$ if and only if $a \cdot e = b \cdot d$'. The rational function containing $\langle a, b \rangle$ is denoted by a/b. The *sum* $a/b + d/e$ of the rational functions a/b, d/e is the rational function $(a \cdot e + b \cdot d)/b \cdot e$, and their *product* $(a/b) \cdot (d/e)$ is $a \cdot d/b \cdot e$.

If an integral domain G contains at least two elements, then, by the proof of Theorem 19, Chapter 2, the set of rational functions over G is a field under the operations defined above, and $G[x]$ is a subring of this field, a polynomial f being identified with the rational function f/I.

We note that a rational function is not a function. It can sometimes be associated with a function in the same way that a polynomial can be associated with a polynomial function, but we will not consider this here. In this section we will be concerned only with the expression of an arbitrary rational function as the sum of simpler rational functions, the so-called expansion in partial fractions.

THEOREM 12. *Let f, g, h be non-0 polynomials over a field $(G, +, \cdot)$. If f and g are relatively prime, then there are unique polynomials q, a, b over $(G, +, \cdot)$ such that*

$$h/(f \cdot g) = q + a/f + b/g,$$

and either $a = 0$ or $\deg a < \deg f$, and either $b = 0$ or $\deg b < \deg g$.

Proof. We first show that q, a, b exist, and then that they are unique. By the division theorem, there are polynomials q, r such that

$$h/(f \cdot g) = q + r/(f \cdot g),$$

where either $r = 0$ or $\deg r < \deg f \cdot g$. Since f and g are relatively prime, there are polynomials c, d such that

$$I = c \cdot f + d \cdot g.$$

Thus,

$$r = c \cdot r \cdot f + d \cdot r \cdot g.$$

The polynomials f, g are non-0 and so, by the division theorem, there are polynomials u, v, a, b such that

$$c \cdot r = u \cdot g + b,$$
$$d \cdot r = v \cdot f + a,$$

and $a = 0$ or deg $a <$ deg f, and $b = 0$ or deg $b <$ deg g. From these equations we get

$$r = b \cdot f + a \cdot g + f \cdot g \cdot (u + v).$$

If $u + v \neq 0$, then deg $f \cdot g \cdot (u + v) \geqslant$ deg $f \cdot g$. But, by the conditions on r, a, and b,

$$\deg f \cdot g \cdot (u + v) = \deg (r - b \cdot f - a \cdot g) < \deg f \cdot g,$$

which is a contradiction, and so $u + v = 0$. Thus

$$h/(f \cdot g) = q + b/g + a/f,$$

where a and b have the required properties.

Now we show that q, a, b are unique. By the conditions on a and b, the polynomials q and $b \cdot f + a \cdot g$ must be respectively the quotient and remainder when h is divided by $f \cdot g$. Thus q and $b \cdot f + a \cdot g$ are uniquely determined by h, f, and g. Suppose that

$$b \cdot f + a \cdot g = b' \cdot f + a' \cdot g,$$

where either $b' = 0$ or deg $b' <$ deg g, and either $a' = 0$ or deg $a' <$ deg f. Since f and g are relatively prime and $(b - b') \cdot f = (a' - a) \cdot g$, f must divide $a' - a$. If $a \neq a'$, then this implies that deg $a' - a \geqslant$ deg f, and this is impossible by the conditions on a and a'. Thus $a' = a$, and similarly $b' = b$. □

THEOREM 13. *If f and g are non-0 polynomials over a field $(G, +, \cdot)$, n is a positive integer, and deg $f < n$ deg g, then there are unique polynomials b_1, b_2, $b_3, \ldots, b_n$ over $(G, +, \cdot)$, each of which has degree less than deg g or is 0, such that*

$$f/g^n = b_1/g + b_2/g^2 + b_3/g^3 + \ldots + b_n/g^n.$$

Proof. Note that if the required b_i do exist, then

$$f = g^{n-1} \cdot b_1 + (g^{n-2} \cdot b_2 + g^{n-3} \cdot b_3 + \ldots + b_n)$$

and $g^{n-2} \cdot b_2 + g^{n-3} \cdot b_3 + \ldots + b_n$ either is 0 or has degree less than deg g^{n-1}. Thus b_1 must be the quotient and $g^{n-2} \cdot b_2 + g^{n-3} \cdot b_3 + \ldots + b_n$ the remainder when f is divided by g^{n-1}. Similarly, if $g^{n-2} \cdot b_2 + g^{n-3} \cdot b_3 + \ldots + b_n$ is divided by g^{n-2}, then the quotient is b_2 and the remainder is $g^{n-3} \cdot b_3 + g^{n-4} \cdot b_4$

$+ \ldots + b_n$, and so on. This shows that if the b_i exist, then they are unique, and it also suggests the method of proof.

Let $b_1, b_2, b_3, \ldots, b_n, r_1, r_2, r_3, \ldots, r_{n-1}$ be polynomials such that

$$f = b_1 \cdot g^{n-1} + r_1$$
$$r_1 = b_2 \cdot g^{n-2} + r_2$$
$$r_2 = b_3 \cdot g^{n-3} + r_3$$
$$\vdots \qquad \vdots$$
$$r_{n-2} = b_{n-1} \cdot g + r_{n-1}$$
$$r_{n-1} = b_n$$

and, for each i, either $r_i = 0$ or $\deg r_i < (n - i) \deg g$. There are such polynomials, by the division theorem. Adding up these n equations, we obtain

$$f = b_1 \cdot g^{n-1} + b_2 \cdot g^{n-2} + b_3 \cdot g^{n-3} + \ldots + b_n.$$

From $f = b_1 \cdot g^{n-1} + r_1$ and $\deg f < n \deg g$, it follows that either $b_1 = 0$ or $\deg b_1 < \deg g$. If $i > 1$, then $r_{i-1} = b_i \cdot g^{n-i} + r_i$, so that, if $b_i \neq 0$, we have $\deg b_i + (n - i) \deg g < (n - i + 1) \deg g$; from which it follows that $\deg b_i < \deg g$. □

By Theorems 12 and 13, and the unique factorization theorem, we can now express every rational function over a field as the sum of a polynomial and rational functions of the form b/a^n, where $\deg b < \deg a$ and a is prime over the field. Such a representation of a rational function is called an expansion of the rational function in *partial fractions*.

EXAMPLE. The rational function

$$(x^6 + 2x^3 + 1)/((x - 1) \cdot (x^2 + 1)^2)$$

over $(\mathbf{R}, +, \cdot)$ must be expressible in the form

$$q + a/(x - 1) + b/(x^2 + 1) + c/(x^2 + 1)^2,$$

where q, b, c are polynomials over $\mathbf{R}$ such that either $b = 0$ or $\deg b < 2$, and either $c = 0$ or $\deg c < 2$, and a is a real number. Over the field of complex numbers, this rational function can be written as

$$q + a/(x - 1) + b/(x + i) + c/(x + i)^2 + d/(x - i) + e/(x - i)^2,$$

where q is a polynomial and a, b, c, d, e are complex numbers. In order to find q, a, b, c, d, e, multiply the rational function and its expansion by $(x - 1) \cdot (x^2 + 1)^2$, and either equate the coefficients in the resulting polynomial equation or assign various values to x. Details of this and more elaborate methods and rules can be found in school algebra textbooks.

EXERCISES

1. Expand the following rational functions in partial fractions:

(i) $x^2/((1+x^2)\cdot(1-x))^2$, over the field of rational numbers;

(ii) as (i), but over the field of complex numbers;

(iii) $1/((x-[2])\cdot(x+[1]))$, over the field of residue classes modulo 5;

(iv) as (iii), but over the field of residue classes modulo 3.

2. Let f, g, and h be non-0 polynomials over a field G, such that $(f,g)\,|\,h$ and $\deg h < \deg f\cdot g$. Show that there are polynomials a, b over G such that

$$h/(f\cdot g) = a/f + b/g,$$

and either $a = 0$ or $\deg a < \deg f$, and either $b = 0$ or $\deg b < \deg g$. Show that a and b are not necessarily uniquely determined by f, g, and h.

3. Let f and g be non-0 polynomials over a field, f having $\deg f$ different roots $a_1, a_2, a_3, \ldots, a_{\deg f}$ and g having degree less than $\deg f$. Show that

(i) $f^{(1)}/f = \sum_{i=1}^{\deg f} 1/(x-a_i)$;

(ii) $(f\cdot f^{(2)} - (f^{(1)})^2)/f^2 = \sum_{i=1}^{\deg f} 1/(x-a_i)^2$;

(iii) $g/f = \sum_{i=1}^{\deg f} g(a_i)/(f^{(1)}(a_i)\cdot(x-a_i))$.

4. Show that, if all the roots $a_1, a_2, a_3, \ldots, a_{\deg f}$ of a polynomial f over $\mathbf{R}$ are distinct and real, and g is a polynomial over $\mathbf{R}$ of degree less than $\deg f - 1$, then

$$\sum_{i=1}^{\deg f} g(a_i)/f^{(1)}(a_i) = 0.$$

5 Polynomials in several variables

Now we will generalize some of the results of the first section of this chapter by considering polynomials over rings of polynomials. Let G be a ring. We have already defined $G[x]$, the ring of polynomials over G, and shown it to be a ring. Thus we can consider $(G[x])[x]$, the ring of polynomials over $G[x]$, and $((G[x])[x])[x]$, the ring of polynomials over $(G[x])[x]$, and so on. In the usual notation, every polynomial in $G[x]$ is of the form

$$a_0 + a_1 x + a_2 x^2 + \ldots$$

where x is a place symbol and the a_i are elements of G, only a finite number of them being non-0. Thus a polynomial in $(G[x])[x]$ is of the above form, where the a_i are polynomials in $G[x]$. In this case the place symbol in the coefficients must be distinguished from the place symbol in the polynomial, and we will use x_1 as the first place symbol and x_2 as the second, so that every polynomial in $(G[x])[x]$ is of the form

$$(a + bx_1 + cx_1^2 + \ldots) + (d + ex_1 + fx_1^2 + \ldots)x_2 + (g + hx_1 + ix_1^2 + \ldots)x_2^2 + \ldots,$$

where a, b, c, d,... are elements of G, only a finite number of them being non-0. Thus, a polynomial in $(G[x])[x]$ is the sum of a finite number of polynomials of the form $cx_1^n x_2^m$, where $c \in G$ and n and m are integers, factors of the form x^0 being deleted from any term in which they occur. We will denote $(G[x])[x]$ by $G[x_1, x_2]$ and refer to an element of $G[x_1, x_2]$ as 'a polynomial in x_1, x_2 over G'.

DEFINITION. Let $(G, +, \cdot)$ be a ring. For each positive integer n, we denote $(G[x_1, x_2, x_3, \ldots, x_{n-1}])[x]$ by $G[x_1, x_2, x_3, \ldots, x_n]$ and refer to an element of $G[x_1, x_2, x_3, \ldots, x_n]$ as a *polynomial in x_1, x_2, x_3, ..., x_n over G*.

REMARKS. (i) $G[x_1, x_2, x_3, \ldots, x_n]$ is a ring, and if G is an integral domain then $G[x_1, x_2, x_3, \ldots, x_n]$ is also an integral domain. This follows from Theorem 1, by induction on n.

(ii) If $n < m$, then $G[x_1, x_2, x_3, \ldots, x_n]$ can be embedded in $G[x_1, x_2, x_3, \ldots, x_m]$ in the same way that G was embedded in $G[x]$ in §1.

(iii) We will always use x_n as the place symbol in a polynomial over $G[x_1, x_2, x_3, \ldots, x_{n-1}]$, so that such a polynomial is the sum of a finite number of polynomials of the form $cx_1^{m_1} x_2^{m_2} x_3^{m_3} \ldots x_n^{m_n}$, where $c \in G$ and m_1, m_2, m_3, ..., m_n are integers, factors of the form x_i^0 being deleted from any term in which they occur.

(iv) We saw, in §1, that if G is a ring with identity, then the polynomial x commutes with every polynomial in $G[x]$. Therefore, if G has an identity, then x_i will commute with every polynomial in $G[x_1, x_2, x_3, \ldots, x_i]$. Also, if $j > i$, then x_i will commute with x_j, because $x_i \in G[x_1, x_2, x_3, \ldots, x_j]$. Thus, the polynomials x_1, x_2, x_3, ..., x_n commute with one another and with all the elements of G, and so commute with all the polynomials in $G[x_1, x_2, x_3, \ldots, x_n]$.

DEFINITION. The *total degree* of a non-0 polynomial f in x_1, x_2, x_3, ..., x_n over a ring G is the smallest integer $\mathrm{Deg}\, f$ such that f is the sum of a finite number of polynomials of the form $cx_1^{m_1} x_2^{m_2} x_3^{m_3} \ldots x_n^{m_n}$, where $c \in G$ and $m_1 + m_2 + m_3 + \ldots + m_n \leqslant \mathrm{Deg}\, f$.

By remark (iii) above, every non-0 polynomial has a unique total degree.

THEOREM 14. *If f and g are non-0 polynomials in x_1, x_2, x_3, ..., x_n over a ring G, then:*

(i) *either $f + g = 0$, or $\mathrm{Deg}\,(f + g) \leqslant \max (\mathrm{Deg}\, f, \mathrm{Deg}\, g)$;*
(ii) *either $f \cdot g = 0$, or $\mathrm{Deg}\, f \cdot g \leqslant \mathrm{Deg}\, f + \mathrm{Deg}\, g$;*
(iii) *if G is an integral domain, then*

$$\mathrm{Deg}\, f \cdot g = \mathrm{Deg}\, f + \mathrm{Deg}\, g.$$

10

Proof. Parts (i) and (ii) follow immediately from the definition of 'total degree' and the properties of rings.

In order to prove (iii), we first note that if m is an integer and h is a non-0 polynomial which is the sum of polynomials of the form $cx_1^{m_1} x_2^{m_2} x_3^{m_3} \ldots x_n^{m_n}$, where $c \in G$ and $m_1 + m_2 + m_3 + \ldots + m_n = m$, then $\operatorname{Deg} h = m$. This is easily proved by induction on n; it is trivial if $n = 1$, and the case $n = s + 1$ follows from the case $n = s$ by considering the leading coefficient of the appropriate polynomial. The details are left for the reader.

Now let f and g be non-0 polynomials in $x_1, x_2, x_3, \ldots, x_n$ over an integral domain G. By the definition of $\operatorname{Deg} f$, we can express f as the sum of polynomials of the form $cx_1^{m_1} x_2^{m_2} x_3^{m_3} \ldots x_n^{m_n}$, where $c \in G$ and $m_1 + m_2 + m_3 + \ldots + m_n \leqslant \operatorname{Deg} f$. Let f' be the sum of those polynomials in this expression of f for which $m_1 + m_2 + m_3 + \ldots + m_n = \operatorname{Deg} f$. Then $f' \neq 0$. We define g' similarly. By the preceding result, $\operatorname{Deg} f = \operatorname{Deg} f'$ and $\operatorname{Deg} g = \operatorname{Deg} g'$. By the definitions of f' and g', either $f - f' = 0$ or $\operatorname{Deg} f - f' < \operatorname{Deg} f$, and either $g - g' = 0$ or $\operatorname{Deg} g - g' < \operatorname{Deg} g$. Also, $f' \cdot g'$ is a sum of polynomials of the form $cx_1^{m_1} x_2^{m_2} x_3^{m_3} \ldots x_n^{m_n}$, where $m_1 + m_2 + m_3 + \ldots + m_n = \operatorname{Deg} f + \operatorname{Deg} g$, and so either $f' \cdot g' = 0$ or $\operatorname{Deg} f' \cdot g' = \operatorname{Deg} f + \operatorname{Deg} g$. Since G is an integral domain, $f' \cdot g' \neq 0$, and so $\operatorname{Deg} f' \cdot g' = \operatorname{Deg} f + \operatorname{Deg} g$. Now consider the equality

$$f' \cdot g' = f \cdot g - f' \cdot (g - g') - (f - f') \cdot g' - (f - f') \cdot (g - g').$$

If $\operatorname{Deg} f \cdot g < \operatorname{Deg} f + \operatorname{Deg} g$, then, by (i), (ii), and the above equality, we would have $\operatorname{Deg} f' \cdot g' < \operatorname{Deg} f + \operatorname{Deg} g$. This is a contradiction, and so $\operatorname{Deg} f \cdot g \geqslant \operatorname{Deg} f + \operatorname{Deg} g$; which, with (ii), proves (iii). $\square$

In §2 we associated a polynomial function from G to G with each polynomial over a ring G. If $f \in G[x_1, x_2, x_3, \ldots, x_n]$ and $a_1, a_2, a_3, \ldots, a_n \in G$, then $f(a_1, a_2, a_3, \ldots, a_n)$ is defined as follows: since f is a polynomial over $G[x_1, x_2, x_3, \ldots, x_{n-1}]$, the substitution of a_n for x_n results in a polynomial in $G[x_1, x_2, x_3, \ldots, x_{n-1}]$, as defined in §2. If a_{n-1} is substituted for x_{n-1} in this polynomial, then the result is a polynomial in $G[x_1, x_2, x_3, \ldots, x_{n-2}]$, and so on. After n such applications of the definition in §2, we have obtained an element of G which we denote by $f(a_1, a_2, a_3, \ldots, a_n)$.

It is important to note that $f(a_1, a_2, a_3, \ldots, a_n)$ is obtained by substituting a_n for x_n, a_{n-1} for $x_{n-1}, \ldots, a_1$ for x_1, *in that order*, into f. For example, let G be a ring with identity, let $f = x_1 x_2$, and let a and b be elements of G such that $a \cdot b \neq b \cdot a$. Then $f(a, b)$ is obtained by substituting b for x_2, with the result $x_1 \cdot b$, which is the polynomial bx_1, and then substituting a for x_1. Thus, $f(a, b) = b \cdot a$. If we first substituted a for x_1, and then b for x_2, the result would be $a \cdot b$, which is not $f(a, b)$.

We have now defined $f(a_1, a_2, a_3, \ldots, a_n)$ for every $f \in G[x_1, x_2, x_3, \ldots, x_n]$

and every sequence $a_1, a_2, a_3, \ldots, a_n$ of n elements from G. Let us denote the set of all sequences of n elements from G by G^n. Then each polynomial $f \in G[x_1, x_2, x_3, \ldots, x_n]$ determines a function $\alpha(f)$ from G^n to G, the value of $\alpha(f)$ at $(a_1, a_2, a_3, \ldots, a_n) \in G^n$ being the ring element $f(a_1, a_2, a_3, \ldots, a_n)$. If G is a commutative ring, then α is a homomorphism from the ring $G[x_1, x_2, x_3, \ldots, x_n]$ to the ring of all functions from G^n to G; this is a generalization of Theorem 6. If G is an infinite field, then α is an injective homomorphism. The proof of this follows from the next theorem in the same way that Theorem 8 followed from Theorem 7.

THEOREM 15. *If G is an infinite field, and f is a non-0 polynomial in $G[x_1, x_2, x_3, \ldots, x_n]$, then there are elements $b_1, b_2, b_3, \ldots, b_n \in G$ such that $f(b_1, b_2, b_3, \ldots, b_n) \neq 0$.*

Proof. We proceed by induction on n. If $n = 1$, the result follows from Theorem 7(iii), p. 120. Let us suppose that the result holds if $n = m - 1$, and let f be a non-0 polynomial $\in G[x_1, x_2, x_3, \ldots, x_m]$. Then f is a polynomial in x_m over the integral domain $G[x_1, x_2, x_3, \ldots, x_{m-1}]$. This integral domain can be embedded in a field F, and so f is a polynomial in x_m over a field and hence, by Theorem 7(iii), it has only a finite number of roots in F. But $G \subseteq G[x_1, x_2, x_3, \ldots, x_{m-1}] \subseteq F$, and G contains an infinite number of elements, so there is an element $b_m \in G$ which is not a root of f. Substitute b_m for x_m in f. The result is a non-0 polynomial $g \in G[x_1, x_2, x_3, \ldots, x_{m-1}]$. By our supposition, there are elements $b_1, b_2, b_3, \ldots, b_{m-1} \in G$, which, if substituted for $x_1, x_2, x_3, \ldots, x_{m-1}$ in g, yield a non-0 element of G. □

6   Symmetric polynomials

Let G be a ring. We have already defined $f(a_1, a_2, a_3, \ldots, a_n)$ for $f \in G[x_1, x_2, x_3, \ldots, x_n]$ and $a_1, a_2, a_3, \ldots, a_n \in G$. More generally, we can substitute polynomials from $G[x_1, x_2, x_3, \ldots, x_n]$ for $x_1, x_2, x_3, \ldots, x_n$. Let f, $g_1, g_2, \ldots, g_n \in G[x_1, x_2, x_3, \ldots, x_n]$. Then $f(g_1, g_2, g_3, \ldots, g_n)$ is defined to be that polynomial in $G[x_1, x_2, x_3, \ldots, x_n]$ which is the result of substituting g_n for x_n, g_{n-1} for $x_{n-1}, \ldots, g_1$ for x_1, in that order, into f.

For example, if G is a ring with identity, then $f = f(x_1, x_2, x_3, \ldots, x_n)$.

DEFINITION. Let G be a ring with identity. A polynomial $f \in G[x_1, x_2, x_3, \ldots, x_n]$ is *symmetric* if $f = f(x_{i_1}, x_{i_2}, x_{i_3}, \ldots, x_{i_n})$ for every permutation $\begin{pmatrix} 1 & 2 & 3 \ldots n \\ i_1 & i_2 & i_3 \ldots i_n \end{pmatrix}$ of $1, 2, 3, \ldots, n$.

EXAMPLES. Let G be a ring with identity and let n be a positive integer. (i) For each integer j such that $1 \leqslant j \leqslant n$, let $\sigma(j, n)$ be the sum of all those polynomials in $G[x_1, x_2, x_3, \ldots, x_n]$ which are of the form $x_{i_1} x_{i_2} x_{i_3} \ldots x_{i_j}$, where i_1, i_2, i_3, ..., i_j are integers such that $1 \leqslant i_1 < i_2 < i_3 < \ldots < i_j \leqslant n$. That is,

$$\sigma(1, n) = x_1 + x_2 + x_3 + \ldots + x_n,$$
$$\sigma(2, n) = x_1 x_2 + x_1 x_3 + \ldots + x_1 x_n + x_2 x_3 + x_2 x_4 + \ldots + x_{n-1} x_n,$$
$$\vdots \qquad \qquad \vdots$$
$$\sigma(n, n) = x_1 x_2 x_3 \ldots x_n.$$

We noted on p. 129 that the polynomials x_1, x_2, x_3, ..., x_n commute with one another. Thus, the polynomials $\sigma(1, n)$, $\sigma(2, n)$, $\sigma(3, n)$, ..., $\sigma(n, n)$ are symmetric.

(ii) If f, g_1, g_2, ..., $g_n \in G[x_1, x_2, x_3, \ldots, x_n]$, and g_1, g_2, g_3, ..., g_n are symmetric, then obviously $f(g_1, g_2, g_3, \ldots, g_n)$ is a symmetric polynomial. In particular, $f(\sigma(1, n), \sigma(2, n), \sigma(3, n), \ldots, \sigma(n, n))$ is a symmetric polynomial.

DEFINITION. Let G be a ring. The *weight* of a polynomial $f \in G[x_1, x_2, x_3, \ldots, x_n]$ is the smallest integer wgt f such that f is a sum of polynomials of the form $c x_1^{m_1} x_2^{m_2} x_3^{m_3} \ldots x_n^{m_n}$, where $c \in G$ and $m_1 + 2m_2 + 3m_3 + \ldots + nm_n \leqslant$ wgt f.

If $\sigma(n, n)$, $\sigma(n-1, n)$, $\sigma(n-2, n)$, ..., $\sigma(1, n)$ are substituted for x_n, x_{n-1}, x_{n-2}, ..., x_1 in a polynomial f, then a typical term $c x_1^{m_1} x_2^{m_2} x_3^{m_3} \ldots x_n^{m_n}$ in f becomes $c \cdot \sigma(1, n)^{m_1} \cdot \sigma(2, n)^{m_2} \cdot \sigma(3, n)^{m_3} \cdot \ldots \cdot \sigma(n, n)^{m_n}$, which is of total degree $m_1 + 2m_2 + 3m_3 \ldots + nm_n$ at most. Thus, either $\mathrm{Deg}\, f(\sigma(1, n), \sigma(2, n), \sigma(3, n), \ldots, \sigma(n, n)) \leqslant$ wgt f, or $f(\sigma(1, n), \sigma(2, n), \sigma(3, n), \ldots, \sigma(n, n)) = 0$. (In fact, if $f \neq 0$, then $\mathrm{Deg}\, f(\sigma(1, n), \sigma(2, n), \sigma(3, n), \ldots, \sigma(n, n)) =$ wgt f. This is an easy consequence of the next theorem, and is set as an exercise.)

It follows easily from the properties of rings that, for any two polynomials f, g in x_1, x_2, x_3, ..., x_n over a ring,

(i) wgt $(f + g) \leqslant$ max (wgt f, wgt g);

(ii) wgt $f \cdot g \leqslant$ wgt $f +$ wgt g.

THEOREM 16. *Let G be a ring with identity, and let f be a symmetric polynomial in $G[x_1, x_2, x_3, \ldots, x_n]$ of total degree m. Then there is a polynomial h in $G[x_1, x_2, x_3, \ldots, x_n]$ of weight m such that $f = h(\sigma(1, n), \sigma(2, n), \sigma(3, n), \ldots, \sigma(n, n))$.*

Proof. Suppose that, for some ring G, the theorem is not true. Then there is a smallest integer n and a symmetric polynomial f in $G[x_1, x_2, x_3, \ldots, x_n]$ of smallest total degree for which the conclusion of the theorem does not hold. That is, there is an integer n and a symmetric polynomial f in $G[x_1, x_2, x_3, \ldots, x_n]$ such that:

(i) If g is a non-0 symmetric polynomial in $G[x_1, x_2, x_3, \ldots, x_m]$ and either (a) $m < n$; or (b) $m = n$ and $\text{Deg } g < \text{Deg } f$; then there is a polynomial $h \in G[x_1, x_2, x_3, \ldots, x_m]$ of weight $\text{Deg } g$ and such that

$$g = h(\sigma(1, m), \sigma(2, m), \sigma(3, m), \ldots, \sigma(m, m)).$$

(ii) There is no polynomial $h \in G[x_1, x_2, x_3, \ldots, x_n]$ of weight $\text{Deg } f$ and such that

$$f = h(\sigma(1, n), \sigma(2, n), \sigma(3, n), \ldots, \sigma(n, n)).$$

We will disprove (ii) and thus prove the theorem.

First, we note that $n > 1$, since $g(x_1) = g(\sigma(1, 1))$ and $\text{Deg } g = \text{wgt } g$ for all non-0 polynomials $g \in G[x_1]$.

Suppose that the polynomial $f(x_1, x_2, x_3, \ldots, x_{n-1}, 0)$ is not 0. Then, by condition i(a) above, there is a polynomial $h \in G[x_1, x_2, x_3, \ldots, x_{n-1}]$ of weight $\text{Deg } f(x_1, x_2, x_3, \ldots, x_{n-1}, 0)$ and such that

$$f(x_1, x_2, x_3, \ldots, x_{n-1}, 0)$$
$$= h(\sigma(1, n-1), \sigma(2, n-1), \sigma(3, n-1), \ldots, \sigma(n-1, n-1)).$$

Let $g = f - h(\sigma(1, n), \sigma(2, n), \sigma(3, n), \ldots, \sigma(n-1, n))$, and suppose that $g \neq 0$. The polynomial g is in $G[x_1, x_2, x_3, \ldots, x_n]$ and is clearly symmetric. By the choice of h,

$$g(x_1, x_2, x_3, \ldots, x_{n-1}, 0) = 0.$$

Thus, $g = x_n \cdot p$, where $p \in G[x_1, x_2, x_3, \ldots, x_n]$ and therefore, because g is symmetric, there is a polynomial $k \in G[x_1, x_2, x_3, \ldots, x_n]$ such that $g = \sigma(n, n) \cdot k$.

The weight of h is $\text{Deg } f(x_1, x_2, x_3, \ldots, x_{n-1}, 0)$, which cannot exceed $\text{Deg } f$, and so $\text{Deg } g \leqslant \text{Deg } f$. Therefore, if $k \neq 0$, we have

$$\begin{aligned} \text{Deg } k &= \text{Deg } g - n \\ &\leqslant \text{Deg } f - n \\ &< \text{Deg } f. \end{aligned}$$

Thus, by i(b), there is a polynomial $q \in G[x_1, x_2, x_3, \ldots, x_n]$ of weight $\text{Deg } k$, such that

$$k = q(\sigma(1, n), \sigma(2, n), \sigma(3, n), \ldots, \sigma(n, n)).$$

Thus

$$\begin{aligned} f = {}&h(\sigma(1, n), \sigma(2, n), \sigma(3, n), \ldots, \sigma(n-1, n)) \\ &+ \sigma(n, n) \cdot q(\sigma(1, n), \sigma(2, n), \sigma(3, n), \ldots, \sigma(n, n)). \end{aligned}$$

The polynomial $h + x_n \cdot q$ has weight not exceeding $\text{Deg } f$, because $\text{wgt } h \leqslant \text{Deg } f$, $\text{wgt } x_n = n$, and $\text{wgt } q = \text{Deg } g - n$. Thus, $\text{Deg } f \leqslant \text{wgt } (h + x_n \cdot q) \leqslant \text{Deg } f$, and so $h + x_n q$ has weight $\text{Deg } f$.

We have now expressed f in the required way, which contradicts (ii).

If $f(x_1, x_2, x_3, \ldots, x_{n-1}, 0) = 0$ or if $g = 0$, then the above argument is easily modified to again contradict (ii), and so the theorem is proved. □

THEOREM 17. *If G is a ring with identity, $h \in G[x_1, x_2, x_3, \ldots, x_n]$, and $h(\sigma(1, n), \sigma(2, n), \sigma(3, n), \ldots, \sigma(n, n)) = 0$, then $h = 0$.*

Proof. If the theorem does not hold then, as in the previous proof, there is a smallest integer n, and a polynomial $h \in G[x_1, x_2, x_3, \ldots, x_n]$ with the smallest total degree, such that the statement of the theorem does not hold. It is easily seen that n must be greater than 1.

The polynomial $h(\sigma(1, n-1), \sigma(2, n-1), \sigma(3, n-1), \ldots, \sigma(n-1, n-1), 0)$ is just $h(\sigma(1, n), \sigma(2, n), \sigma(3, n), \ldots, \sigma(n, n))$ evaluated at $x_n = 0$, and so it is 0. Thus, $h(x_1, x_2, x_3, \ldots, x_{n-1}, 0) = 0$, so there is a polynomial $k \in G[x_1, x_2, x_3, \ldots, x_n]$ such that $h = x_n \cdot k$. Since Deg $k =$ Deg $h - 1$, it follows that $k(\sigma(1, n), \sigma(2, n), \sigma(3, n), \ldots, \sigma(n, n)) \neq 0$, and therefore

$$h(\sigma(1, n), \sigma(2, n), \sigma(3, n), \ldots, \sigma(n, n))$$
$$= \sigma(n, n) \cdot k(\sigma(1, n), \sigma(2, n), \sigma(3, n), \ldots, \sigma(n, n)) \neq 0.$$

This is a contradiction, which proves the theorem. □

From the preceding theorem we conclude that the polynomial h of Theorem 16 is uniquely determined by f.

Let G be a ring with identity and, for all positive integers i, n, let

$$s(i, n) = \sum_{j=1}^{n} x_j^i.$$

That is,

$$s(1, n) = x_1 + x_2 + x_3 + \ldots + x_n,$$
$$s(2, n) = x_1^2 + x_2^2 + x_3^2 + \ldots + x_n^2,$$

and so on. Each polynomial $s(i, n)$ is obviously symmetric and of total degree i and so, by Theorems 16 and 17, there is a unique polynomial h of weight i such that

$$s(i, n) = h(\sigma(1, n), \sigma(2, n), \sigma(3, n), \ldots, \sigma(n, n)).$$

We will now derive a set of equations called *Newton's formulae* which provide an easy iterative method for finding h for any n and i.

First, it is convenient to put $a(1, n) = -\sigma(1, n)$, $a(2, n) = \sigma(2, n)$, and generally to put $a(i, n) = (-1)^i \sigma(i, n)$. Then it is easily shown, by induction on n, that

$$(x_{n+1} - x_1) \cdot (x_{n+1} - x_2) \cdot (x_{n+1} - x_3) \cdot \ldots \cdot (x_{n+1} - x_n)$$
$$= x_{n+1}^n + a(1, n) x_{n+1}^{n-1} + a(2, n) x_{n+1}^{n-2} + \ldots + a(n, n).$$

The polynomials $x_{n+1} - x_1$, $x_{n+1} - x_2$, $x_{n+1} - x_3, \ldots,$ $x_{n+1} - x_n$, are polynomials in x_{n+1} over a commutative subring of $G[x_1, x_2, x_3, \ldots, x_n]$. Thus, letting $x_{n+1} = x_i$, we have, by Theorem 6

$$x_i^n + a(1, n) x_i^{n-1} + a(2, n) x_i^{n-2} + \ldots + a(n, n) = 0$$

for $i = 1, 2, 3, \ldots, n$. If the i-th of these n equations is multiplied by x_i^{m-n}, where $m \geqslant n$, and the resulting n equations are added together, we obtain the equation:

(i) $s(m, n) + a(1, n) s(m - 1, n)$
$$+ a(2, n) s(m - 2, n) + \ldots + a(n, n) s(m - n, n) = 0,$$

where we let $s(0, n) = n$. For each integer $m \geqslant n$ we have an equation (i), and these equations enable us to find $s(m, n)$ in terms of the $\sigma(i, n)$ if $s(m - 1, n)$, $s(m - 2, n)$, $s(m - 3, n), \ldots,$ $s(m - n, n)$ have already been so expressed. Thus it only remains to find $s(n - 1, n), s(n - 2, n), s(n - 3, n), \ldots,$ $s(1, n)$ in terms of the $\sigma(i, n)$.

We will now show that

(ii) $s(m, n) + a(1, n) s(m - 1, n) + a(2, n) s(m - 2, n) + \ldots$
$$+ a(m - 1, n) s(1, n) + ma(m, n) = 0$$

for $m = 1, 2, 3, \ldots, n - 1$. This enables us to express $s(m, n)$ in terms of $s(m - 1, n)$, $s(m - 2, n)$, $s(m - 3, n), \ldots,$ $s(1, n)$, and hence in terms of the $\sigma(i, n)$.

We proceed by induction on n. It is clear that (ii) holds if $n = 1$. Suppose that (ii) holds for $n = r - 1$. It follows easily from the definitions that, for $i = 1, 2, 3, \ldots, r$,

$$s(i, r) = s(i, r - 1) + x_r^i;$$

$$a(i, r) = a(i, r - 1) - x_r \cdot a(i - 1, r - 1), \text{ if } 2 \leqslant i \leqslant r;$$

and $a(1, r) = a(1, r - 1) - x_r.$

From these equations it follows that

$$s(m, r) + a(1, r) s(m - 1, r) + a(2, r) s(m - 2, r) + \ldots$$
$$+ a(m - 1, r) s(1, r) + ma(m, r)$$

$$= \big(s(m, r - 1) + a(1, r - 1) s(m - 1, r - 1) + \ldots + ma(m, r - 1) \big)$$
$$- x_r \cdot \big(s(m - 1, r - 1) + a(1, r - 1) s(m - 2, r - 1) + \ldots$$
$$+ (m - 1) a(m - 1, r - 1) \big).$$

If $m = 1, 2, 3, \ldots,$ or $r - 2$, then both the bracketed terms are 0 by our assumption. If $m = r - 1$, the first term is 0 by (i), and the second term is 0

by our assumption. Thus, by the principle of induction, we have established (ii) for all positive integers n and all $m = 1, 2, 3, \ldots, n-1$.

We note that, if $a(i, n)$ is defined to be 0 for all $i > n$, then both (i) and (ii) are included in the one statement:

$$s(m, n) + a(1, n)\,s(m-1, n) + a(2, n)\,s(m-2, n) + \ldots + ma(m, n) = 0$$

for all positive integers m, n.

EXERCISES

1. Let G be a ring with identity, let a and b be elements of G such that $a \cdot b \neq b \cdot a$, and let $f = x^2$, $g = b + x$. Find $f(g)$, $(f(g))(a)$, and $f(g(a))$.

2. Let G be a ring, let $f, g_1, g_2, \ldots, g_n$ be polynomials in $x_1, x_2, x_3, \ldots, x_n$ over G, and let $a_1, a_2, a_3, \ldots, a_n$ be elements of G which commute with every element of G. Show that, if $a_n, a_{n-1}, a_{n-2}, \ldots, a_1$ are substituted for $x_n, x_{n-1}, x_{n-2}, \ldots, x_1$, in that order, into $f(g_1, g_2, g_3, \ldots, g_n)$, then the result is

$$f(g_1(a_1, a_2, a_3, \ldots, a_n), g_2(a_1, a_2, a_3, \ldots, a_n), \ldots, g_n(a_1, a_2, a_3, \ldots, a_n)).$$

3. Let f be a polynomial over a ring G with identity, and let a be an element of G such that $f(a) = 0$. Show that there is a polynomial k, over G, such that $f = x \cdot k$.

4. Show that

$s(2, n) = \sigma(1, n)^2 - 2\sigma(2, n)$;

$s(3, n) = \sigma(1, n)^3 - 3\sigma(1, n)\,\sigma(2, n) + 3\sigma(3, n)$;

$s(4, n) = \sigma(1, n)^4 - 4\sigma(1, n)^2\,\sigma(2, n) + 4\sigma(1, n)\,\sigma(3, n) + 2\sigma(2, n)^2 - 4\sigma(4, n)$;

first, by the method of the proof of Theorem 16, and then by using Newton's formulae.

5. Find $a^2 + b^2 + c^2$, if a, b, c are the roots of $x^3 - 3x^2 + 1$.

6. Find the polynomial whose roots are $a^{-2} + b^{-2}$, $a^{-2} + c^{-2}$, $b^{-2} + c^{-2}$, where a, b, c are the roots of $x^3 - 2x + 1$.

7. Show that the set of all symmetric polynomials in $x_1, x_2, x_3, \ldots, x_n$ over a ring G, is a subring of $G[x_1, x_2, x_3, \ldots, x_n]$ which is isomorphic to $G[x_1, x_2, x_3, \ldots, x_n]$.

8. Show that if a non-0 polynomial $f \in G[x_1, x_2, x_3, \ldots, x_n]$ has weight w, then $f(\sigma(1, n), \sigma(2, n), \sigma(3, n), \ldots, \sigma(n, n))$ has total degree w.

9. Let $a_1, a_2, a_3, \ldots, a_n$ be complex numbers. Show that there are complex numbers $b_1, b_2, b_3, \ldots, b_n$ such that

$$\sigma(i, n)(b_1, b_2, b_3, \ldots, b_n) = ai$$

for $i = 1, 2, 3, \ldots, n$.

10. Express

$$x_1^3 x_2 + x_1^3 x_3 + x_2^3 x_1 + x_2^3 x_3 + x_3^3 x_1 + x_3^3 x_2$$

as a polynomial in $\sigma(1, 3)$, $\sigma(2, 3)$, $\sigma(3, 3)$, by the method of the proof of Theorem 16.

11. Let G be a ring with identity, let $f \in G[x_1, x_2, x_3, \ldots, x_n]$. Show that the set of those permutations on $1, 2, 3, \ldots, n$ which leave $f(x_1, x_2, x_3, \ldots, x_n)$ unchanged is a subgroup of S_n. By considering $x_1 x_2 + x_3 x_4$, show that S_4 has a subgroup of order 8.

12. Our definition of $s(i, n)$ can obviously be extended to negative integers i. Find an iterative method for obtaining $s(i, n)$ for $i < 0$, in terms of the $\sigma(i, n)$.

INDEX OF SYMBOLS

(The numbers refer to the pages on which the symbols are introduced.)

$\in$, $\notin$	1
$\{a, b, c, \ldots\}$	1
$\{x \mid —\}$	1
$=$, $\neq$	1
$\subseteq$, $\supseteq$	1
$\cup$, $\cap$	1
$\langle a, b \rangle$	2
$[a]$	2
$f(a)$	3
$f(C), f^{-1}(E)$	4
$\mathbf{Z}^{+}$, s	5
$\{1, 2, 3, \ldots\}$	6
$\mathbf{Z}$	11
$\leqslant$, $\geqslant$, $<$, $>$	13, 39, 46, 100
$\lvert a \rvert$	15, 40, 48, 57
$]a, b[$	16
f_i, $(f_i)_i$	18
Σ, Π	20, 38, 46, 55, 65
$b \mid a$	24, 113
(a, b)	25, 113
$[a, b]$	29
$a \equiv b \; (n)$	30
a/b	31, 37, 46, 55, 125
$\mathbf{Q}$	37
$\mathbf{R}$	43
$\sqrt[n]{a}$	51
$\mathbf{C}$	54
i	55
$\bar{z}$	57
$\arg z$	59
$(G, \cdot)$	66

$f \circ g$	73
S_n	75
$\begin{pmatrix} 1 & 2 & 3 & \ldots & n \\ f(1) & f(2) & f(3) & \ldots & f(n) \end{pmatrix}$	75
$(a_1, a_2, a_3, \ldots, a_s)$	76
I_n	76
A_n	79
G/K	88
$G - K$	88
$H \cdot K, h \cdot K, K \cdot h$	89
$(G, +, \cdot)$	93
$(G, +, \leqslant)$	100
$(G, +, \cdot, \leqslant)$	100
$\log_a x$	104
$G[x]$	109
$\deg f$	109
$\max(a, b, c, \ldots)$	111
$f^{(1)}, f^{(n)}$	121
$G[x_1, x_2, x_3, \ldots, x_n]$	129
$\mathrm{Deg} f$	129
$f(a_1, a_2, a_3, \ldots, a_n)$	130, 131
$\sigma(j, n)$	131
$\mathrm{wgt} f$	132
$s(i, n)$	134

GENERAL INDEX

Abelian, 9, 67
Absolute value, 15, 40, 48, 57
Additive group of a field, 94
Alternating group, 79
Amplitude, 59
Archimedean, 101
Argument, 59
Arithmetic mean, 52
Associative law, 9, 12, 21, 23, 45, 55, 65
Automorphism, 92
Average, 52

Bijection, 3, 73, 84
Binary operation, 64
Bounded above, 16, 51
Bounded below, 16, 50, 104

Cancellation law, 9, 12, 31
Canonical homomorphism, 88, 97
Cauchy sequence, 40, 49, 57
Cauchy's inequality, 52
Cayley, 84
Chinese remainder theorem, 34
Closed, 65
Coefficient, 109
Commutative law, 9, 12, 22, 23, 45, 55, 67, 94
Commute, 110
Complex number, 54
Composition, 73
Congruences, solution of, 33
Congruent, 30
Conjugate, 57
Constant polynomial, 110
Contain, 76
Contain exactly a elements, 16, 17
Continuous, 51
Converge, 49
Convex, 107
Coset, 89
Cycle, 76
Cyclic, 68, 72

Dedekind, 5
Degree, 109
Degree of a zero polynomial, 111
Demoivre's formula, 60
Derivative of a polynomial, 121
Difference group, 88, 97
Difference ring, 98
Dirichlet box principle, 24

Disjoint, 1, 76
Distributive law, 9, 12, 93
Divide, 24, 113
Division theorem, 24, 112
Divisor, 24, 113
Divisor of 0, 94
Dyck, 84

Element, 1
Embedding, 10, 38, 46, 55, 96
Equal sets, 1
Equivalence class, 2
Equivalence relation, 2
Euclid's algorithm, 25, 115
Even permutation, 78
Existence of $\mathbf{Z}^+$, 5

Factor group, 88
Fermat's theorem, 32
Field, 94
Finite group, 71
Finite sequence, 18
Finite set, 17
Function, 3
Fundamental theorem of algebra, 56, 62, 123

General associative and commutative laws, 21 ff.
Generator, 68
Geometric mean, 52
Greater than, 13, 39, 46
Greatest common divisor, 25, 113
Greatest lower bound, 50, 104
Greatest member, 16
Group, 66

Halperin, 78
Hölder, 101
Homomorphic image, 81
Homomorphism, 13, 81 ff., 95

Ideal, 27, 97
Identity in a group or ring, 66, 93, 94
Index, 93
Induction, 6
Infinite sequence, 18
Infinite set, 17
Initial element, 5
Injection, 3
Inner automorphism, 92

142 GENERAL INDEX

Integer, 11
Integral domain, 94, 110
Intersection, 1
Inverse in a group, 66, 93
Isomorphic, 83
Isomorphism, 81 ff., 95
i-th coefficient, 109
i-th term, 18

Jordan, 84

Kernel, 87, 97
Klein 4-group, 85

Lagrange, 91
Largest member, 16, 111
Leading coefficient, 109
Least common multiple, 29
Least member, 15
Least upper bound, 51
Less than, 13, 39, 46
Limit, 41, 49, 58
Linear combination, 25
Logarithmic function, 82, 104, 107
Lower bound, 16, 50, 104

Mahler, 34
Monic polynomial, 113
Moved element, 77
Multiple of an integer, 29
Multiplicative group, 94
Multiplicity of a root, 120

Negative integer, 13
Newton's formulae, 134
Normal subgroup, 87
Number of elements in a set, 16

Odd permutation, 78
One-one, 3
Open set, 51
Operation, 64
Order of a group, 71, 91
Order of an element in a group, 69, 91
Ordered pair, 1
Order-homomorphism, 107
Order-isomorphism, 101

Parallelogram, 58
Pairwise-disjoint, 1
Partial fractions, 127
Peano, 5
Permutation, 75
Place symbol, 109
Point, 58
Polar coordinates, 59

Polar form, 59
Polynomial, 108, 129
Polynomial function, 119
Positive cone, 106
Positive integer, 5, 6, 12
Positive real number, 52
Power of an element in a group, 67
Prime, 27, 115
Primitive n-th root of unity, 61
Principle of induction, 7
Product of a finite sequence of group
    elements, 65
Product of a finite sequence of integers,
    20
Product of complex numbers, 55, 58
Product of integers, 11, 12
Product of polynomials, 109
Product of positive integers, 9, 12
Product of rational functions, 125
Product of rational numbers, 37
Product of real numbers, 43
Product of residue classes, 30
Product of subsets of a group, 89
Pythagoras's theorem, 58

Quasi-ordered set, 106
Quotient, 24, 112
Quotient group, 88

Rational function, 125
Rational number, 37
Real number, 43
Relation, 2
Relatively prime, 27, 115
Remainder, 24, 112
Remainder theorem, 123
Residue class, 30
Restriction, 64
Ring, 13, 93, 94
Root of a polynomial, 120
Root of multiplicity n, 120
Root of unity, 60

Sequence, 18
Set, 1
Smallest member, 15
Subfield, 95
Subgroup, 70, 71
Subring, 95
Subset, 1
Successor function, 5
Sum of a finite sequence of group
    elements, 65
Sum of finite sequence of integers, 20
Sum of complex numbers, 54, 58
Sum of integers, 11, 12
Sum of polynomials, 109
Sum of positive integers, 8, 12

Sum of rational functions, 125
Sum of rational numbers, 37
Sum of real numbers, 43
Sum of residue classes, 30
Sum of subsets of a group, 89
Surjection, 3
Symmetric group, 75
Symmetric polynomial, 131

Term, 18
Theorem of the means, 53
Total degree, 129
Totally ordered set, 100
Transformation, 79

Transposition, 76
Triangle inequality, 58

Union, 1
Unique factorization theorem, 28, 116
Upper bound, 16, 51

Vector, 58

Wallis, 58
Weierstrass's inequality, 52
Weight, 132
Well-ordering theorem, 15

Zero ring, 94